Student Worktext Level A

A Reason For Spelling ® Student Worktext - Level A
2017 Edition

EAN#: 978-0-936785-25-7
ISBN#: 0-936785-25-X
TL#: SPSWTA2018WC

Published by Concerned Communications, LLC
P.O. Box 1000, Siloam Springs, AR 72761

Authors: Rebecca Burton, Eva Hill, Leah Knowlton, Kay Sutherland
Layout: Mark Decker, Melissa Habermas
Copy Editor: Mary Alice Hill • Story Editor: Tricia Schnell
Proofreaders: Daniel Swatsenberg, Marcie Smith

Created by MOE Studio, Inc.
Black and White Illustrations: James McCullough
Colorization: Mark Decker
Design/Layout: Greg Hauth, Greg Sutherland
Project Leaders: Greg Sutherland, Eva Hill

For more information about A Reason For Handwriting®, A Reason For Spelling®,
A Reason For Science®, & A Reason For Guided Reading®, visit our website:

www.AReasonFor.com

Phonics Section
Day 1 through Day 34

In this **Student Worktext, Level A,** the Phonics Section
(yellow edge tabs) offers a series of **fun activities** based on
partner letters and **sounds** to help strengthen a student's
phonics skills. If you do one page per day, you can complete
this section in approximately six weeks.

If you are using a "stand-alone" Phonics program, this section
can simply be used for review and reinforcement.

A | Poetry Connection

Name _____

The Apples

Apples, crunchy apples, hanging in the tree,
Apples, juicy apples, Jesus made for me.

Down comes an apple with a little stem,
Down, down, down, when I shake the limb.

Apples, crunchy apples, hanging in the tree,
Apples, juicy apples, Jesus made for me.

Down come two apples . . . (continue)

Look at the first letter in each row. Draw a circle around the other letter in the row that is the same.

1.	b	a	b	c	d
2.	g	g	h	i	j
3.	q	p	q	r	s
4.	d	b	c	d	e
5.	p	m	n	o	p
6.	t	s	t	u	v
7.	l	j	k	l	m
8.	h	f	g	h	i
9.	k	k	l	m	n

10.	r	r	s	t	u
11.	n	m	n	o	p
12.	m	j	k	l	m
13.	f	d	e	f	g
14.	j	h	i	j	k
15.	y	w	x	y	z
16.	v	u	v	w	x
17.	w	t	u	v	w
18.	z	w	x	y	z

3

Name _____

A, a go together.
A, a are partner letters.
Color the apples that have partner letters on them.

1.  A a

2. F j

3. K k

4.  X y

5. E f

6. Z x

7.  R r

8. H h

9. J i

10.  V v

11. M w

12. T i

13.  N n

14. I t

15. L j

Name _____

The Squirrel

I saw a squirrel, then he saw me,
And so he ran around the tree.

He peeked, and chattered, "Scold, scold, scold,"
But then, he got a little bold.

He scampered close, around and 'round,
He whirled his way down to the ground.

I think that God had lots of fun,
Creating squirrels to twirl and run.

S, s go together.
S, s are partner letters.
Find the partner letters and draw
a circle around both of them.

1. B C d b	**2.** D d C b	**3.** D G g o	**4.** P q n O
5. s C S o	**6.** p g G B	**7.** Q P b q	**8.** P p c D
9. b G B o	**10.** q C c P	**11.** S O g s	**12.** b P D d
13. O p o Q	**14.** D C P p	**15.** q g Q S	**16.** o c C G

Name _____

Follow the dots from **A** to **Z**. What secret animal do you see? Write the first letter of its name in the space below.

_quirrel

Name _____

My Balloon

I went to the circus and got something new,
A great big balloon, so round and so blue!

If I should let go, I'd lose it I know,
So I hold the string tightly, and let the wind blow!

Look at the first letter in each row.
Draw a circle around each letter in the row that is the same.

1. b	b	q	p	b	b
2. p	d	p	p	b	p
3. d	q	d	d	d	p
4. q	b	q	d	q	q
5. d	b	d	d	p	d
6. b	b	b	d	b	q
7. p	p	q	p	p	b
8. q	d	q	p	q	q
9. p	p	b	p	p	d
10. d	b	b	d	d	d
11. q	p	q	p	q	q
12. b	b	b	d	b	d

Name _____

Circle the letter for each beginning sound,
then write the letter on the line below the picture.

Sounds of /b/, /d/, /p/, /kw/

Day **3**

1.

b
d
p
q

_____
- - - - - - - -
_____

2.

b
d
p
q

_____
- - - - - - - -
_____

3.

b
d
p
q

_____
- - - - - - - -
_____

4.

b
d
p
q

_____
- - - - - - - -
U
_____

5.

b
d
p
q

_____
- - - - - - - -
_____

6.

b
d
p
q

_____
- - - - - - - -
_____

7.

b
d
p
q

_____
- - - - - - - -
_____

8.

b
d
p
q

_____
- - - - - - - -
_____

9.

b
d
p
q

_____
- - - - - - - -
U
_____

Name _____

In The Beehive

(Make a fist)
Here is the beehive,
But where are the bees?

(Tuck thumb inside fist)
Hidden inside, where nobody sees.
Here they come buzzing,
Out of their hive,

(Open fist and count each finger)
One, — two, — three, — four, — five!

Sounds of /b/, /d/, /p/

Day

4

Circle each picture if its name begins with the same sound as the letter in that row.

b

1.

2.

3.

4.

d

5.

6.

7.

8.

p

9.

10.

11.

12.

Help the bees get out of the hive.
Color the honeycomb
boxes that have
b, **d**, **p**, or **q**
on them.

Differences of b, d, p, q

Day
4

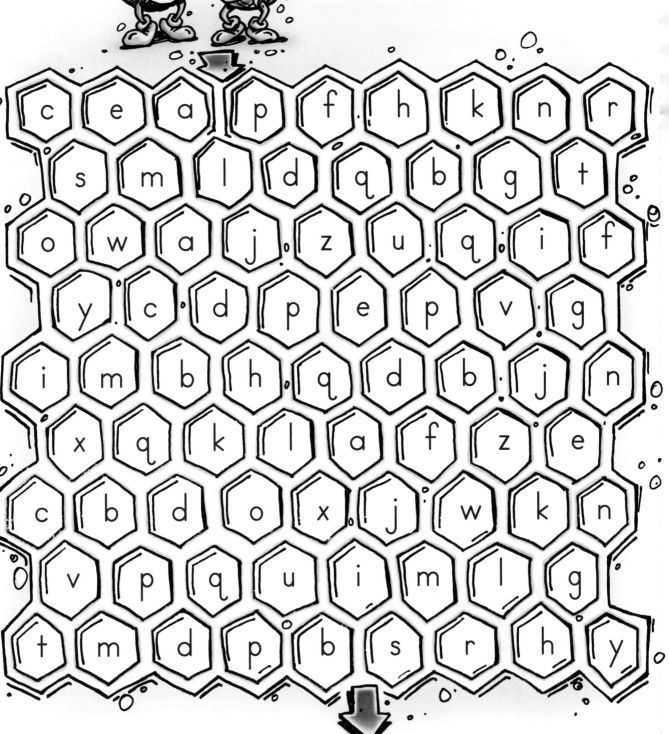

Ten Green Frogs

Ten green frogs,
With winking, blinking eyes.
Sitting on a mossy log,
Catching dragonflies.

One frog jumped into the bog,
Splash! Nine frogs.

Nine green frogs . . .
(continue to zero)

Write the letter for the beginning sound
to complete each word.

1.

__ed

2.

__og

3.

__ig

4.

__ox

5.

__ie

6.

__all

7.

__en

8.

__at

Follow the dots from **A** to **Z**.
What secret animal do you see?
Write the first letter of its name in the space below.

_____

_rog

The Farmer

The farmer helps us every day,
He gathers the eggs the chickens lay.
He goes to the barn to milk the cows,
Then out to the field where he plows and plows!

He plants the seeds to grow the wheat,
And corn and oats we like to eat.
And when night comes, he kneels to pray,
"Thank you, God, for my busy day."

Circle each picture if its name
contains the same short vowel sound
as the letter in that row.

1.  **2.**  **3.** **4.**

a

5. **6.** **7.** **8.**

o

9. **10.** **11.** **12.**

a

13

B Phonics

Circle the name of each picture.

1.

rat   hat   hand

2.

box   fox   fog

3.

tip   tap   top

4.

and   an   ant

5.

man   can   cat

6.

rip   rack   rock

7.

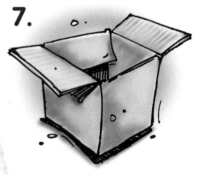

bat   bug   box

8.

map   man   wax

9.

log   dog   lot

Five Little Ducklings

Five little ducklings,
Waddle, waddle, waddle!
Jumped into the farmer's pond,
Their feet began to paddle.

When their mother called to them,
Quack, quack, quack!
Four little ducklings,
Swam right back.

Four little ducklings . . . (continue to one)

Partner Letters

Day 7

D, d go together.
D, d are partner letters.
Circle the partner letters in the pairs below.

1. I j   **2.** L k   **3.** D d   **4.** Q q

5. G g   **6.** P q   **7.** O o   **8.** M m

9. J l   **10.** N n   **11.** Q q   **12.** G q

13. M n   **14.** L i   **15.** K k   **16.** J j

15

Name _____

Write the letter for each beginning sound.

1.

_____
- - - - - - -
_____

2.

_____
- - - - - - -
_____

3.

_____
- - - - - - -
_____

4.

_____
- - - - - - -
_____

5.

_____
- - - - - - -
_____

6.

_____
- - - - - - -
_____

7.

_____
- - - - - - -
_____

8.

_____
- - - - - - -
___ U

9.

_____
- - - - - - -
_____

10.

_____
- - - - - - -
___ U

11.

_____
- - - - - - -
_____

12.

_____
- - - - - - -
___ U

The Crab

We have a crab in our science lab,
I like him very well.
His tank has water and lots of sand,
He lives inside a shell.

I take him from his tank, sometimes,
So I can watch him walk.
His legs come out, his claws stick out,
His eyes are on a stalk.

He likes to walk along my arm,
And he can climb a tree.
I really like this hermit crab,
And I'm sure he likes me!

Sound of /e/

Day

8

Color each shell that has a word
with the sound of **/e/**.

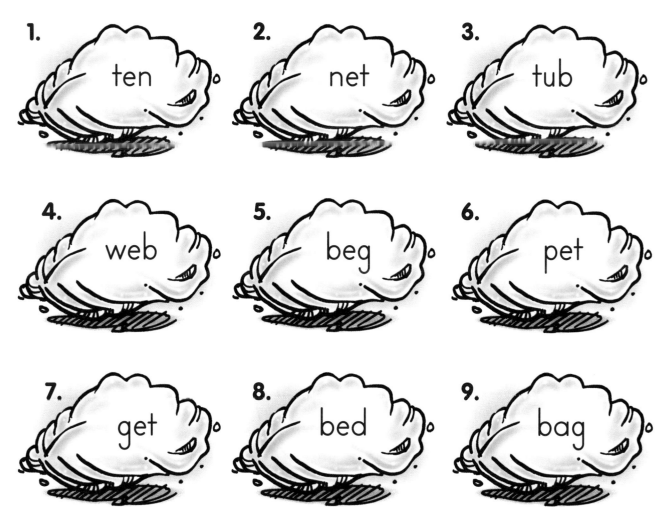

1. ten

2. net

3. tub

4. web

5. beg

6. pet

7. get

8. bed

9. bag

Name _____

Circle the name of each picture.

1.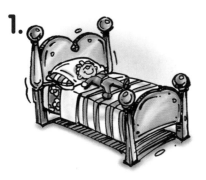

bed   fed   led

2.

jet   pet   wet

3.

leg   egg   beg

4.

ten   bent   tent

5.

nest   not   just

6.

went   man   men

7.

west   well   web

8.

tan   ten   tin

9.

bill   sell   bell

A Poetry Connection

Name _____

Baby Chick

I found a little egg on a summer's day,
Out in the barn in a nest of hay.

Peep, peep, peep and peck, peck, peck,
The egg cracked open and out came a neck!

Soon that little chick was up and about,
I'm glad Jesus showed him how to get out.

Look at the word on each egg in the nest. Color the egg if the word begins with the letter **b**.

2. bug
4. wing
3. ball
5. bus
1. bag
6. duck
7. egg
8. boat
9. bat
10. leg
11. nest

19

Circle the letter for each beginning sound,
then write the letter on the line below the picture.

1.

b

c _____

p _____

2.

b

c _____

p _____

3.

b

c _____

p _____

4.

b

c _____

p _____

5.

b

c _____

p _____

6.

b

c _____

p _____

7.

b

c _____

p _____

8.

b

c _____

p _____

9.

b

c _____

p _____

A Poetry Connection

Name _____

Fireflies

The fireflies are out tonight,
And in our yard they look so bright.
God made each with a little light!

I'm a light in darkness, too,
And I'll shine like the fireflies do.
Because God's love comes shining through!

Circle each picture in the row whose
name begins like the first picture.

1.  |

2.  |

3.  |

4.  |

Circle each picture whose name says **i**, as in **lit**.

Sound of /i/

Day
10

1.

2.

3.

4.

5.

6.

7.

8.

9.

10.

11.

12.

13.

14.

15.

16.

Name _____

The Carpenter

The carpenter's hammer goes rap, rap, rap,
And his saw goes see, saw, see.
He hammers, rap, rap, and saws, see, saw,
As he's building a house for me.

Jesus was a carpenter too, you know,
And His saw went see, saw, see.
But now He lives in heaven above,
Where He's building a mansion for me!

Circle each picture if its name begins
with the same sound as the letter in that row.

1.

2.

3.

4.

B **Phonics**

Name _____

Write the letter for each beginning sound on the first line.
Write the letter for each ending sound on the second line.

1.

____ | ____

2.

____ | ____

3.

____ | ____

4.

____ | ____

5.

____ | ____

6.

____ | ____

7.

____ | ____

8.

____ | ____

9.

____ | ____

10.

____ | ____

11.

____ | ____

12.

____ | ____

Winter Clothes

I'm wearing a hat, and fluffy ear muffs.
My gloves, and my mittens are pinned to my cuffs.

I've layers of pants, and two sweaters besides.
My three pairs of socks make my feet very wide.

My boots are too tight, like the scarf 'round my throat,
And I don't think my mother can zip up my coat!

Look at each word. Color the space blue if the word begins with **m** like **mitten**. Color the space red if the word begins with **n** like **nose**.

Color the other word spaces yellow. You will find something that warms you on a cold day.

Sounds of /m/, /n/

Day
12

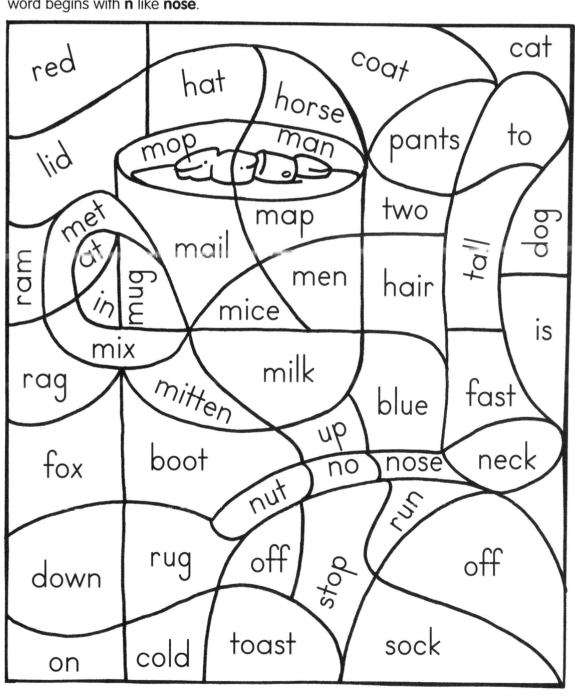

25

Circle the letter for each beginning sound,
then write the letter on the line below the picture.

1.

m

n _____
....
_____

2.

m

n _____
....
_____

3.

m

n _____
....
_____

4.

m

n _____
....
_____

5.

m

n _____
....
_____

6.

m

n _____
....
_____

7.

m

n _____
....
_____

8.

m

n _____
....
_____

9.

m

n _____
....
_____

The Fire Truck

F is for the fire truck,
Painted flaming red.
F is for the firefighters,
Sleeping in their beds.

The firefighters hurry fast,
When the siren blows,
Pulling on their boots and coats,
And other special clothes.

Off goes the fire truck,
Down the road so fast,
All the other cars and trucks,
Must wait for it to pass.

Up comes the ladder,
Out comes the hose,
When the fire is put out,
Back home, the fire truck goes.

Sound of /u/

Day
13

Circle the pictures that have
the sound of **/u/** in the middle.

1.

2.

3.

4.

5.

6.

7.

8.

9.

Write the letter for each beginning sound.

1.
_____
_____
_____

2.
_____
_____
_____

3.
_____
_____
_____

4.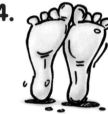
_____
_____
_____

5.
_____
_____
_____

6.
_____
_____
_____

7.
_____
_____
_____

8.
_____
_____
_____

9.
_____
_____
_____

10.
_____
_____
_____

11.
_____
_____
_____

12.
_____
_____
_____

Tomorrow

I run the water,
In the tub, tub, tub.
I jump right in,
And I scrub, scrub, scrub.

My yellow towel,
Gets me dry, dry, dry.
I'm off to bed,
I won't cry, cry, cry.

I kneel right down,
By my bed, bed, bed.
Then jump right in,
When my prayers are said.

Can't wait until tomorrow,
No, I can't, can't, can't.
Cousins June and John are coming,
And my uncle and my aunt.

Draw bubbles around the pairs
that are partner letters.

1. Sc

2. Jj

3. Nw

4. Hh

5. Gg

6. Yz

7. Rr

8. Aa

9. Bd

10. Mn

11. Oo

12. Lf

13. Db

14. Qq

15. Pp

16. Tt

Write the letter for each beginning sound.

1.
_____

2.
_____

3.
_____

4.
_____

5.
_____

6.
_____

7.
_____

8.
_____

9.
_____

10.
_____

11.
_____

12.
_____

Sunburn

I built a castle in the sand,
My dad swam in the ocean.
My sister burned instead of tanned,
She should have used some lotion.

I loved the water and the waves,
But next time I'll be wiser.
I'm sunburned too. My face is red,
Next time I'll wear my visor.

Circle each picture if its name begins with
the same sound as the letter in that row.

Sounds of /v/, /w/

Day
15

1.

2.

3.

4.

Circle the letter for each beginning sound,
then write the letter on the line below the picture.

1.

W

V _____

2.

W

V _____

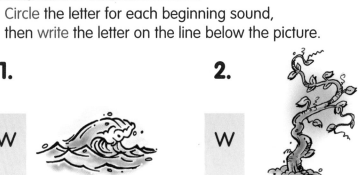

3.

W

V _____

4.

W

V _____

5.

W

V _____

6.

W

V _____

7.

W

V _____

8.

W

V _____

9.

W

V _____

Listening and Tired

When I go to bed at night,
I sometimes lie awake,
And listen to the evening sounds,
God's little creatures make.

I hear the crickets singing near;
I hear the hoot of owls.
The frogs chirp in the meadow grass,
And sometimes coyotes howl.

When morning comes, I'm tired,
Because I didn't get much sleep.
It seems like all the birds are up,
And they begin to cheep.

They even rise before the sun,
So I just lie and squirm.
I don't know why they're up so soon;
I guess they want that worm!

Write the letter for each beginning sound
on the line below the picture.

1.

_____

2.

_____

3.

_____

4.

_____

5.

_____

6.

_____

7.

_____

8.

_____

Name _____

Look at the notes. Beside each note is a picture of something that begins with the sound of /k/ or /s/. Color the note blue if the picture name begins with the sound of /s/ as in **sing**. Color the note red if the picture name begins with the sound of /k/ as in **keep**.

Sounds of /k/, /s/

Day 16

1.

2.

3.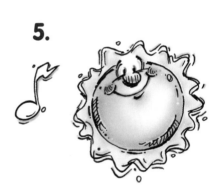

4.

5.

6.

7.

8.

9.

Fuzzy Wuzzy

Fuzzy, wuzzy caterpillar,
Crawled along a twig,
Even though his fuzz stuck out,
He wasn't very big.

Then, one day when I went out,
I found a chrysalis,
I wondered if a butterfly,
Would soon hatch out of this.

And just when I could hardly stand,
To wait another day,
A yellow butterfly came out,
And gently, flew away.

X, x go together.
X, x are partner letters.
Circle the caterpillars that have
partner letters above them.

X   x

1. Xx

2. zZ

3. Zx

4. Yy

5. xX

6. xW

7. Zz

8. xY

9. yY

10. Wv

11. Yz

12. Ww

Name _____

On the butterfly, color each space orange
that has a word with the letter **x**.
Color each space black that has
a word with the letter **z**.

Sounds of /ks/, /z/

Day
17

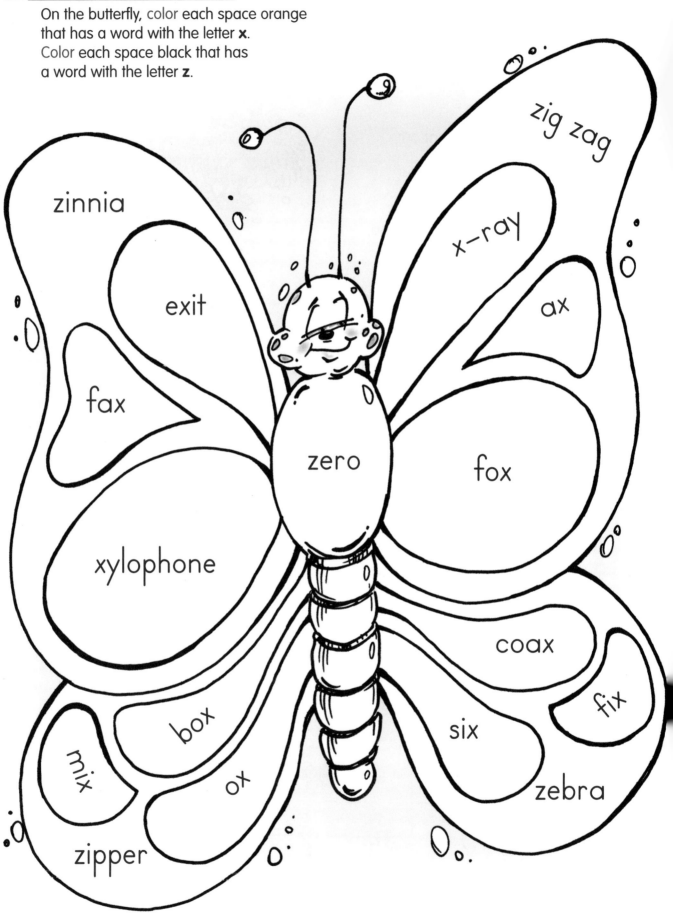

A Poetry Connection

Name _____

Wiggle Jiggle

Inchworms hump and small snakes wiggle,
Grasshoppers jump and beetles jiggle.

Kangaroos bounce and jaguars stalk,
Cats pounce and turtles walk.

Robins hop and snails creep,
Ponies clop and cougars leap.

But God made me, so if I please,
I can move like any of these!

Write the letter for each beginning sound on the first line.
Write the letter for each ending sound on the second line.

1.

2.

3.

4.

5.

6.

7.

8.

Name _____

Cross out letters in each row as listed. Write the remaining letters on the lines to form a word.

Cross Out the Letters – a b c d e

1. | j | c | b | u | a | m | d | p | e |

__ __ __ __ __
__ __ __ __ __

frog

Cross Out the Letters – m n o p q

2. | m | w | p | n | a | o | l | q | k |

__ __ __ __
__ __ __ __

turtle

Cross Out the Letters – w x y z

3. | s | w | t | z | a | l | y | k | x |

__ __ __ __ __
__ __ __ __ __

jaguar

Write the name of the above animal that moves slowest on land.

__ __ __ __ __ __
_____

Alphabet Review

Day
18

Name _____

God is Good

God is good to me and you!
And now before the day is through,
I want to thank my God above,
For watching over me with love.

I thank Him for this happy day,
For friends, for food, for work, and play.
I thank Him for my family,
And all the things they do for me.

God helps me do the things I should,
To be obedient, kind and good.
He keeps me safe through night and day.
And so, to God, each night I pray.

Look at each group of words on the windows.
If all three words rhyme, color the window.
If they do not all rhyme, put an **X** on the window.

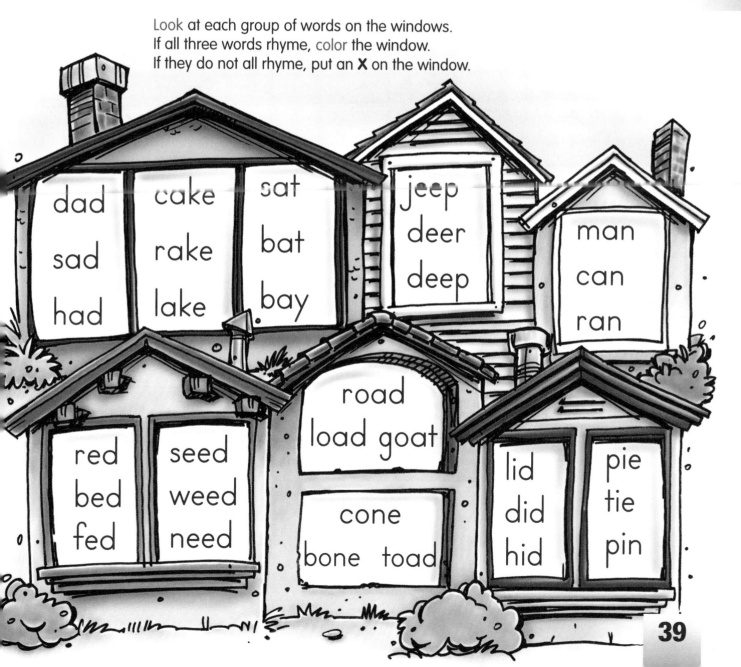

dad
sad
had

cake
rake
lake

sat
bat
bay

jeep
deer
deep

man
can
ran

red
bed
fed

seed
weed
need

road
load goat

cone
bone toad

lid
did
hid

pie
tie
pin

Name _____

Write the letter for each vowel sound on the line below the picture.

1.

d g

2.

m m

3.

b g

4.

d d

5.

s n

6.

f x

7.

h n

8.

w b

9.

p g

10.

c t

11.

l d

12.

h g

A Poetry Connection

**Name** _____

### Day At The Beach

Way down by the ocean,
Way down by the sea,
We spent the whole morning,
My mom, dad, and me.

A cool breeze was blowing,
So we kicked and we splashed,
We watched the waves breaking,
On rocks, with a crash.

We looked for bright seashells,
We played volleyball,
We built sandy castles,
Big, wide, and tall.

God made the oceans,
And filled up the sea,
But wider and deeper,
Is His love for me!

Circle the name of each picture.

1.

log   dog   lot

2.

tap   pat   top

3.

hat   hot   hit

4.

ball   bat   box

5.

dog   dig   dad

6.

top   pit   pot

Sound of /o/

Day
20
Sound of /o/

Day
20
fullSound of /o/

Day
20

41

Circle the word that best completes each sentence,
then write the word on the line.

1.

Bob is

_____

very _____ .   hot   hop

2.

He takes off

_____

his _____ .   socks   sacks

3.

He sits on

_____

a _____ .   rack   rock

4.

He gets in the water

_____

with his _____ .   dog   dig

5.

The sand

_____

is _____ .   sad   soft

Name _____

The Storm

(children tap on desk with fingers)

Rat a tat tat, rat a tat tat,
Spotting the windowpane.
Oh, how I like to sit indoors,
And watch it gently rain.

(children clap their hands)
(lift hands and bring down with fingers
wiggling to show rain pouring)
(open and close fist to make flashes)

Boomity boom, boomity boom,
Thunder smashes and crashes.
Then the rain comes pouring down,
While the lightning flashes.

(pretend to put on boots)
(jump up and down)

After the storm, I dress up warm,
And put on my galoshes.
Out in the puddles I jump and slide,
While the mud just squishes and squashes.

Circle each picture if its name begins with
the same sound as the letter in that row.

1.

p

2.

qu

3.

g

B **Phonics**

Name _____

Write the letter for each beginning sound on the first line.
Write the letter for each ending sound on the second line.

1.

___**u**___ | _____

2.

_____ | _____

3.

_____ | _____

4.

_____ | _____

5.

___**u**___ | _____

6.

_____ | _____

7.

___**u**___ | _____

8.

_____ | _____

9.

_____ | _____

10.

_____ | _____

11.

_____ | _____

12.

_____ | _____

A Poetry Connection

Name _____

The Noise of the Band

The band came marching down the street,
Midst "ooh's!" and "ah's!" and tapping feet.

The cymbals crashed, the trumpets blared,
The drums made thunder in the air.

The flutes were shrill, the band passed near,
And I am surprised that I can still hear!

Write the letter for each beginning sound,
then write the letter for each ending sound.

1.

_____   a

2.

_____   oa

3.

_____   o

4.

_____   an

5.

_____   u

6.

_____   a

7.

_____   u

8.

_____   um

9.

_____   u

10.

_____   oa

11.

_____   i

12.

_____   a

Name _____

Circle the pictures in each row whose names rhyme.

1.

2.

3.

4.

A Poetry Connection

Name _____

Sliding

At the park we like to slide,
Down, down, down we swiftly glide.

'Round to the ladder, up to the top,
Down again, down again, off with a hop.

Circle the name of each picture.

1.

rode   ripe   rope

2.

dive   duck   have

3.

duck   tuck   luck

4.

van   had   hand

5.

red   run   rag

6.

sun   sad   sit

Name _____

Look at the letters that go down the slide. Say each sound, then slide the sounds together to form a word. Look at the pictures in the row and circle the one that matches the word.

1. r a t

2. d o g

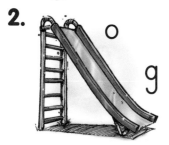   

3. r u n

4. d u c k

5. r u g

A New Friend

I saw a bed and table,
And then a big divan,
More furniture and boxes,
In a great, big moving van!

I saw a boy near my size,
That's moving in next door.
I'll have a friend to play with,
Won't be lonely anymore.

I'll say my prayers at bedtime,
And ask the Lord above,
To bless my friend across the yard,
And help me share God's love.

Circle the name of each picture.

1.

box   fox   find

2.

fork   fold   flat

3.

dive   fish   five

4.

fun   fan   far

5.

fin   fist   fast

6.

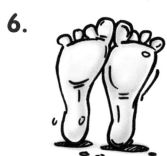

feet   flat   tea

B Phonics

Circle each picture if its name contains the same short vowel sound as the letter in that row.

1. **a**

2. **e**

3. **i**

4. **o**

5. **u**

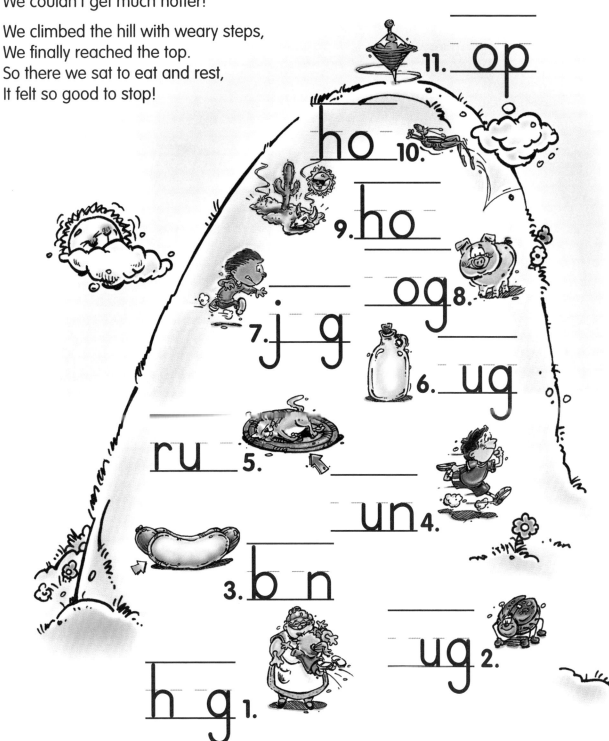

A Poetry Connection

Name _____

To The Top Of The Hill

We set out hiking one fine day,
We carried food and water.
We hiked and hiked, the sun shone bright,
We couldn't get much hotter!

We climbed the hill with weary steps,
We finally reached the top.
So there we sat to eat and rest,
It felt so good to stop!

11. _o_p

ho 10.

9. ho

og 8.

7. j_g

6. _ug

ru_ 5.

_un 4.

3. b_n

ug 2.

h_g 1.

Start at the bottom of the page and write the missing letter that completes the word which names the picture.

Move up to the next number and, by changing one letter from the first word, write the word that goes with the second picture. Continue up the hill.

Name _____

Circle the pictures that have the sound
of **/u/** in the middle.

1.

2.

3.

4.

5.

A Poetry Connection

Name _____

The Little Turtle

This is my little turtle,
I keep him in a box.
He has a bowl to drink from,
He has some climbing rocks.

I like this little turtle,
That Jesus made for me.
I'll keep him for a day or two,
But then, I'll set him free.

Write the missing vowel on the line under each picture.

1.

p __ n

2.

s __ x

3.

b __ g

4.

h __ t

5.

__ gg

6.

p __ p

7.

g __ m

8.

t __ n

Circle the name of each picture.

1.

six   ax   mix

2.

lad   lid   did

3.

mat   mix   mitt

4.

sing   sank   sink

5.

fan   fin   if

6.

fill   hide   hill

7.

did   bad   bib

8.

fix   fast   fist

9.

pig   dig   pie

Name _____

The Train

Clickety, clickety, clickety, clack,
Train wheels singing down the track.

As I wave, the whistle blows,
The engineer smiles because he knows.

I'll be waiting when he comes back,
Clickety, clickety, clickety, clack.

If the name of the picture begins with
the sound of **/l/**, write **l** on the first line.
If the name of the picture ends with
the sound of **/l/**, write **l** on the second line.

Sound of /l/

Day
27

1.

____ | ____

2.

____ | ____

3.

____ | ____

4.

____ | ____

5.

____ | ____

6.

____ | ____

7.

____ | ____

8.

____ | ____

55

Name _____

Circle the letter for each beginning sound,
then write the letter on the line below the picture.

1.

l
k
t

_____
_____
_____

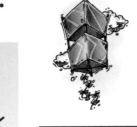

2.

n
g
k

_____
_____
_____

3.

k
h
i

_____
_____
_____

4.

k
n
t

_____
_____
_____

5.

t
c
o

_____
_____
_____

6.

m
l
k

_____
_____
_____

7.

k
s
p

_____
_____
_____

8.

k
b
c

_____
_____
_____

9.

n
s
k

_____
_____
_____

Name _____

Hungry

Everyone is sleeping,
Is sleeping in their bed.
But I am not, I'm wide awake,
And wanting to be fed.

So, I'll go to the kitchen,
To get a pan and spoon.
And if I bang it loud enough,
I'll wake up someone — soon!

Write the letter for each beginning sound
on the first line. Write the letter for each
ending sound on the second line. Circle each
picture whose name begins with the sound of **/m/**.

1.   2.   3.   4.

5.   6.   7.   8.

Circle the name of each picture.

1.

net   nest   fun

2.

tan   ten   nuts

3.

nose   dog   nurse

4.

nine   none   ten

5.

pine   pan   nap

6.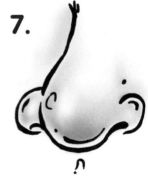

land   nice   nail

7.

sun   nose   rose

8.

nest   mess   rest

9.

moon   sun   man

A Poetry Connection

Window Boxes

I planted pansies in a box,
And added several purple phlox.

Then daisies, mums, and daffodils,
With countless merry, yellow frills.

I added bright petunias bold,
Some zinnias, and marigolds.

And now my flower box is done,
So I will set it in the sun!

Look at each group of words
on the window boxes.
If all three words rhyme,
color the flowers in that box.

game   tame   name

bake   take   tame

nail   mail   pail

Circle the letter for each ending sound.
Place an **X** on the picture if the name
of the picture ends with the sound of /**ks**/.

1.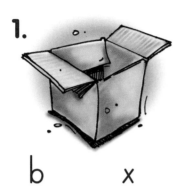

b   x

2.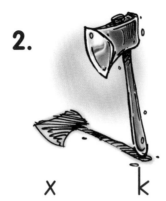

x   k

3.

k   x

4.

t   k

5.

k   x

6.

x   s

7.

w   x

8.

k   x

9.

x   s

Name _____

My New Kite

I have a new kite. I want to try it,
I've asked my friend to help me fly it.

But, if this wind keeps up so strong,
I'm sure my kite won't last for long!

Circle each picture that begins
with the sound of **/w/**.

1.

2.

3.

4.

5.

6.

7.

8.

9.

Hidden on this page is a picture of something that needs wind. Color the space blue if the word begins with **w**.

Color the space red if the word begins with **v**.
Color the space yellow if the word begins with **y**.

Sounds of /v/, /w/, /y/

Day
30

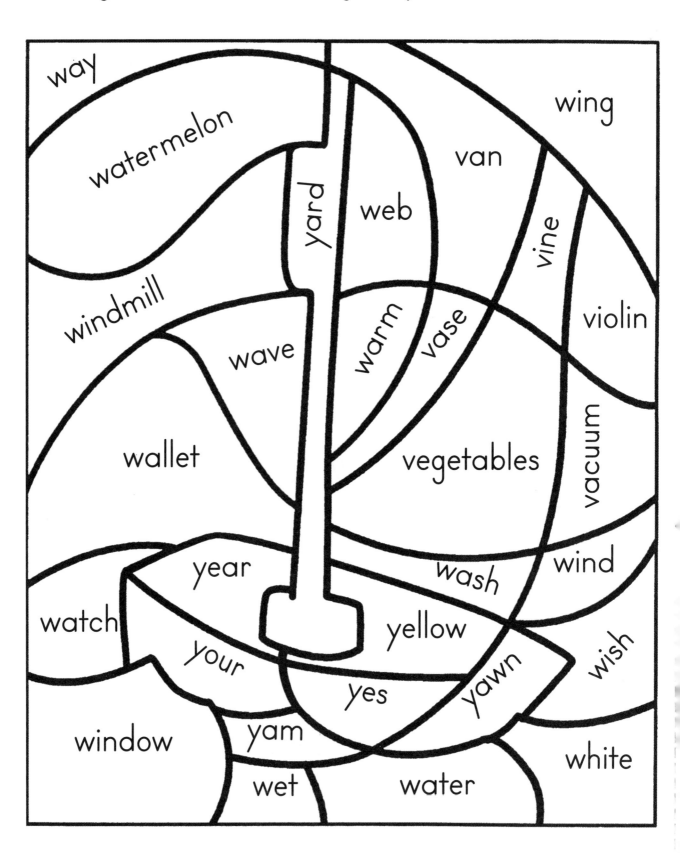

62

Exercise

God made me to hop and skip,
He made my muscles strong and fit.

I exercise, and keep my body strong,
God is wise! I'll praise Him all day long.

Read the words in the Word Bank.
Say each letter in the word, then
look in the puzzle to find that same word.
Circle each word you find.

```
G X C V B N Z J
C L R M J O K E
N K C J O B A L
F Y J U G I S L
T J A M O B D Y
J E E P L A F U
E S J J E T G D
I U J A C K E T
G S H R K J H F
```

Word Bank

JUMP	JEEP	JOB	JOG	JOKE	JESUS
JAM	JUG	JET	JELLY	JAR	JACKET

B **Phonics**

Circle the name of each picture.

Name _____

1.

cane   cone   come

2.

nose   hose   hive

3.

tune   tug   tube

4.

cute   cube   cub

5.

ran   rain   rake

6.

glue   gate   gift

Every Time

Every time I see a little creature crawl,
Every time I see a pretty snowflake fall,
I know God planned the world carefully.
He made everything extraordinarily.

Every time I see a shady maple tree,
Every time I see fish swimming in the sea,
I will thank the Lord for His creation.
Everything He made is a sensation.

Every time I see the lightning light the sky,
Every time I see a hummingbird zoom by,
I will thank the Father for His perfect plan,
And remember that He holds me in His hand.

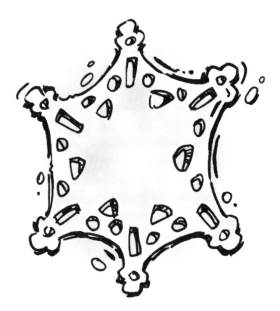

Circle each picture if its name begins
with the same sound as the letter in that row.

1. y

2. z

3. y

Decide what letter is missing in each word and write it in the box to complete the puzzle. Now, copy each letter in order on the lines at the bottom to find the secret word.

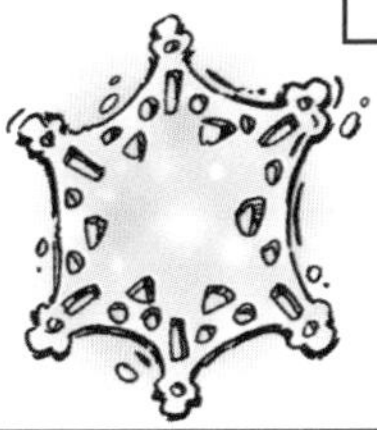

		u	n	
z		b	r	a
y		r	d	
		n	o	w
z	e	r		
w	i		t	e	r
		i	x	

What is the secret word?

___ ___ ___ ___ ___ ___

___ ___ ___ ___ ___ ___

___ ___ ___ ___ ___ ___

Animals From A to Z

Ant, Bear, Crocodile, Dog,
Emu, Fish, Goose, Hedgehog,

Iguana, Jaguar, Kangaroo,
Ladybug, Moose, Nightingale, too.

Owl, Porcupine, Quail, Rhinoceros,
Swan, Turtle, Upside-down catfish,

Vulture, Walrus, Xenops bird,
Yak, and Zebra, now you've heard

Our alphabet animals, A to Z.
God made them all for you and me.

Fill in the missing letter that comes
between the given letters.

1. m ___ o

2. a ___ c

3. g ___ i

4. o ___ q

5. x ___ z

6. t ___ v

7. j ___ l

8. b ___ d

9. ___ n

Write the missing letters that come
before and after the given letter.

10. ___ i ___

11. ___ s ___

12. ___ x ___

13. ___ w ___

14. ___ v ___

15. ___ m ___

16. ___ k ___

17. ___ h ___

18. ___ b ___

B Phonics

Follow the dots from **A** to **Z**.
What secret animal do you see?
Write the first letter of its name
on the line below.

_____ eer

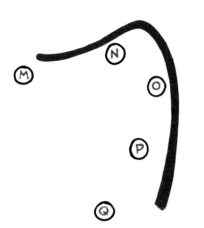

Dear Parent,

   We are about to begin our first Spelling unit containing four weekly lessons. A set of seven words, plus three challenge words, will be studied each week. All the words will be reviewed in the fifth week.

   Values, based on each Scripture listed below, will be featured in that week's lesson.

Lesson 1	Lesson 2	Lesson 3	Lesson 4
an	get	dog	big
man	let	God	dig
ran	bed	on	it
can	red	off	sit
cat	tell	got	hit
at	well	not	did
dad	yes	mom	hid
☆ thank	☆ help	☆ frog	☆ kid
☆ add	☆ best	☆ box	☆ still
☆ ask	☆ next	☆ odd	☆ quit
Psalm 136:1	Psalm 71:8	Prov. 16:9	Prov. 12:22

A | Preview

Write each word as your teacher says it.

Name _____

1. _____

2. _____

3. _____

4. _____

5. _____

6. _____

7. _____

Challenge Words

 _____

_____

_____

Scripture

Psalm 136:1

Name _____

Write each word in the correct Word Shape Boxes.
Next, in the Word Shape Boxes, color the letter
that spells the sound of /a/ in each word.
Circle words that begin with the sound of /a/.

1. an

2. man
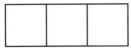

3. ran

4. can
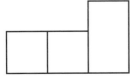

5. cat

6. at
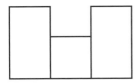

7. dad

☆ **Challenge**

Draw a Shape Box around each letter:

t h a n k   a d d   a s k

C Hide and Seek

Name _____

Circle a cookie for each word you spell correctly.

D Other Word Forms

Using the words below, follow instructions given by your teacher.

added	cats	thankful
adding	daddy	thanks
asked	men	
asking	run	
cans	running	

E Fun Ways to Spell

Initial the box of each activity you finish.

1.  ☐

Spell your words with crayons.

3.  ☐

Spell your words out loud.

2.  ☐

Spell your words with sidewalk chalk.

4.  ☐

Spell your words in damp sand.

F Word Scramble

Name _____

Unscramble the letters to make a spelling word.
Write the word on the line.

1. **ta** 2. **tac** 3. **add** 4. **cna**

_____

5. **nar** 6. **nam** 7. **na** ☆ **kanth**

_____

☆ **sak**

☆ **dda**

Word Bank

an	ran	cat	dad	☆ add
man	can	at	☆ thank	☆ ask

G Dictation

Listen and write the missing words.

1. That _____ is _____ my _____ .

2. Apples _____ be red.

3. My _____ _____ away.

H Proofreading

One word in each pair is misspelled.
Fill in the oval by the misspelled word.

1. ⚪ aan
   ⚪ man

2. ⚪ ran
   ⚪ bab

3. ⚪ mna
   ⚪ at

4. ⚪ kan
   ⚪ an

5. ⚪ dad
   ⚪ kat

6. ⚪ att
   ⚪ can

☆ ⚪ thak
   ⚪ ran

☆ ⚪ cat
   ⚪ aks

☆ ⚪ abb
   ⚪ ask

I Game

Name _____

Beth left her Spelling book in the truck. Lead the way by moving one space each time you or your team spell a word correctly from this week's word list.

Remember : God is good. He loves us even when we're not lovable.

J Journaling

Finish this thank-you letter to God:
Dear God, Thanks for _____.
Love, _____ (Remember to sign your name!)

76

A Preview

Write each word as your teacher says it.

1. _____

2. _____

3. _____

4. _____

5. _____

6. _____

7. _____

Challenge Words

_____

_____

_____

Scripture

Psalm 71:8

77

B Word Shapes

Name _____

Write each word in the correct Word Shape Boxes.
Next, in the Word Shape Boxes, color the letter box
that spells the sound of /e/ in each word.
Circle Word Shape Boxes with double consonants.

1. get

2. let

3. bed

4. red

5. tell

6. well

7. yes

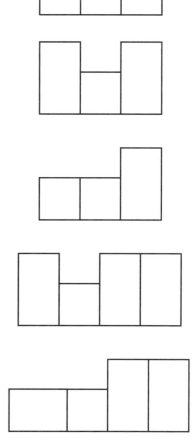

⭐ **Challenge**

Draw a Shape Box around each letter:

h e l p   b e s t   n e x t

C Hide and Seek

Name _____

Circle a cookie for each word you spell correctly.

D Other Word Forms

Using the words below, follow
instructions given by your teacher.

bedding	got	telling
beds	helping	told
better	lets	
gets	letting	
getting	redder	

E Fun Ways to Spell

Initial the box of each activity you finish.

1.

Spell your words with puzzles.

3.

Spell your words with rhythm instruments.

2.

Spell your words on the clothesline.

4.

Spell your words with shaving cream.

Write the words from each group in ABC order.

Words With /e/

Lesson 2

let
get
red
bed
yes
well
tell
well
help
best
next

1. _____ _____

2. _____ _____

3. _____ _____

4. _____ _____

☆ _____ _____

A B C D E F G H I J K L M N O P Q R S T U V W X Y Z

a b c d e f g h i j k l m n o p q r s t u v w x y z

G Dictation

Name _____

Listen and write the missing words.

1. _____ will _____ it.

2. The _____ in _____ is not _____.

3. _____ your _____ we said, " _____ ."

H Proofreading

One word in each pair is misspelled.
Fill in the oval by the misspelled word.

1. ○ red
   ○ tel

2. ○ git
   ○ ran

3. ○ yes
   ○ reb

4. ○ well
   ○ lett

5. ○ yse
   ○ can

6. ○ let
   ○ beb

☆ ○ help
  ○ besk

☆ ○ neks
  ○ ask

☆ ○ hep
  ○ bed

I Game

God gives us people to love and help us. God gave Alex his big brother Matthew to play ball with him and to encourage him.

Circle one softball for each word you or your team spell correctly from this week's word list.

Remember: Never stop praising God for all He has done for you!

J Journaling

Write this sentence: **God sent _____ to help me today.** Fill in the blank with the name of a helper you know.

A Preview

Write each word as your teacher says it.

Name _____

1. _____

2. _____

3. _____

4. _____

Challenge Words

5. _____   _____

_____

6. _____   _____

7. _____   _____

Scripture

Proverbs 16:9

Name _____

Write each word in the correct Word Shape Boxes.
Next, in the Word Shape Boxes, color the letter
that spells the sound of **/o/** or **/ô/** in each word.

1. dog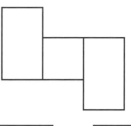

2. God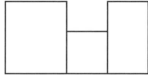

3. on

4. off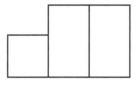

5. got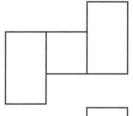

6. not

7. mom

☆ **Challenge**
Draw a Shape Box around each letter:

frog   box   odd

C Hide and Seek

Name _____

Circle a cookie for each word you spell correctly.

D Other Word Forms

Using the words below, follow
instructions given by your teacher.

boxed	frogs	mother
boxes	get	oddest
boxing	getting	odds
dogs	gotten	

E Fun Ways to Spell

Initial the box of each activity you finish.

1.

Spell your words with crayons.

3.

Spell your words from the letter box.

2.

Spell your words with an eraser.

4.

Spell your words with finger paint.

Unscramble the letters to make a spelling word.
Write the word on the line below.

Words With /o/ or /ô/

Lesson **3**

1. dGo _____

2. no _____

3. omm _____

4. tgo _____

5. ton _____

6. gdo _____

7. fof _____

⭐ xbo _____

⭐ dod _____

⭐ gorf _____

Word Bank

dog	on	got	mom	⭐ box
God	off	not	⭐ frog	⭐ odd

86

G Dictation

Name _____

Listen and write the missing words.

1. My _____ _____ _____

the _____.

2. We _____ a _____.

3. My _____ _____

_____ _____ work.

H Proofreading

One word in each pair is misspelled.
Fill in the oval by the misspelled word.

1. ○ dag
   ○ God

2. ○ onn
   ○ off

3. ○ gto
   ○ mom

4. ○ nat
   ○ off

5. ○ on
   ○ Gdo

6. ○ oof
   ○ got

☆ ○ forg
  ○ odd

☆ ○ next
  ○ boks

☆ ○ od
  ○ not

I Game

Cross out each **a**, **k**, and **s** with a big **X** to find the hidden spelling words.

Lightly, color the boxes you did not mark so you can see your spelling words better.

a	k	s	G	o	d	a	k	s
k	s	a	k	f	r	o	g	k
o	n	a	k	s	a	n	o	t
s	a	o	f	f	k	s	a	k
a	k	s	a	b	o	x	k	s
k	s	a	k	s	a	k	s	a
s	a	k	a	a	k	s	a	k
g	o	t	s	a	d	o	g	k
a	k	s	a	k	s	a	k	s
o	d	d	k	m	o	m	s	a

Remember: Always let God direct you in your plans.

J Journaling

Fill in the blank with the name of someone you like to plan with: _____ **can help me make plans.**

A Preview

Write each word as your teacher says it.

1. _____

2. _____

3. _____

4. _____

5. _____

6. _____

7. _____

Challenge Words

⭐ _____

⭐ _____

⭐ _____

Scripture

Proverbs 12:22

Name _____

Write each word in the correct Word Shape Boxes.
Next, in the Word Shape Boxes, color the letter
that spells the sound of **/i/** in each word.
Circle words that begin with the sound of **/i/**.

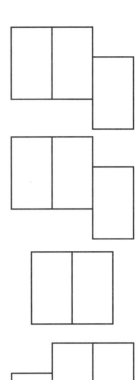

1. big

2. dig

3. it

4. sit

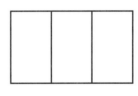

5. hit

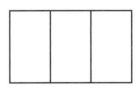

6. did

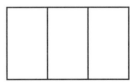

7. hid

⭐ **Challenge**

Draw a Shape Box around each letter:

 k i d   s t i l l   q u i t

C Hide and Seek

Name _____

Circle a cookie for each word you spell correctly.

D Other Word Forms

Using the words below, follow
instructions given by your teacher.

bigger	hidden	kidding	sitting
biggest	hide	kids	
digs	hits	quits	
do	hitting	sat	
dug	its	sits	

E Fun Ways to Spell

Initial the box of each activity you finish.

1.

Spell your words with puzzles.

3.

Spell your words while clapping.

2.

Spell your words with soap.

4.

Spell your words with play dough.

Find and circle 9 words.

Words With /i/

Lesson
4

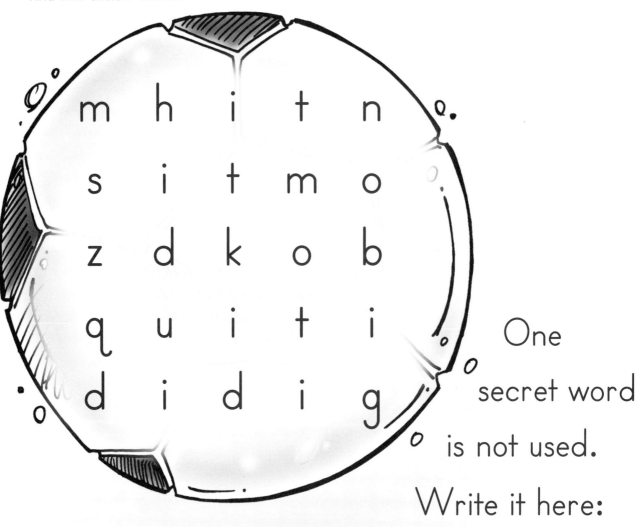

```
m  h  i  t  n
s  i  t  m  o
z  d  k  o  b
q  u  i  t  i
d  i  d  i  g
```

One
secret word
is not used.

Write it here:

_____

_____

Word Bank

big	it	hit	hid	☆ still
dig	sit	did	☆ kid	☆ quit

92

G Dictation

Name _____

Listen and write the missing words.

1. We _____ to _____
the _____ ball.

2. _____ you _____ and
read _____ ?

3. He _____ to _____ .

H Proofreading

One word in each pair is misspelled.
Fill in the oval by the misspelled word.

1. ○ tell
   ○ het

2. ○ fid
   ○ sit

3. ○ bigg
   ○ did

4. ○ et
   ○ dig

5. ○ hid
   ○ stt

6. ○ big
   ○ ded

☆ ○ cid
  ○ it

☆ ○ hit
  ○ kwit

☆ ○ stil
  ○ best

I | Game

Place a game piece over each word your teacher says and spells. When you get five game pieces in a row, raise your hand and say, "Spelling is fun!"

big	an	get	sit	red
hit	did	kid	it	still
dig	can	FREE	got	on
hid	man	tell	off	let
quit	cat	ran	bed	dog

hit	did	hid	still	dig
dad	yes	big	mom	not
cat	tell	FREE	bed	on
can	got	kid	red	off
it	can	quit	let	sit

Remember: Make life happier by keeping your promises.

J | Journaling

Write this sentence in your journal:
I feel _____ when I keep a promise.
Fill in the blank to finish the sentence.

A Test-Words

Write each word as your teacher says it.

1. _____

2. _____

3. _____

4. _____

5. _____

6. _____

7. _____

8. _____

☆ Test-Challenge Words

Write each challenge word
as your teacher says it.

Scripture

Psalm 33:3

In the story from Lesson 3, Beth and Luke asked God to help them decide which dog would be best for their family.
Circle one bowl of dog food for each review word you or your team spell correctly.

C **Test-Sentences**

Name _____

The underlined word in each sentence is misspelled. Write the sentences on the lines below, spelling each underlined word correctly.

<u>Cen</u> you sing songs?

1. _____

Miss Jensen will <u>tel</u> us when to start.

2. _____

D **Test-Proofreading**

One word in each pair is misspelled.
Fill in the oval by the misspelled word.

1. ◯ ran
   ◯ un

2. ◯ at
   ◯ st

3. ◯ ren
   ◯ on

4. ◯ beb
   ◯ did

5. ◯ well
   ◯ nom

6. ◯ bed
   ◯ dib

7. ◯ sit
   ◯ gat

8. ◯ mom
   ◯ wel

9. ◯ att
   ◯ got

 Test-Challenge Words

Write each challenge word
as your teacher says it.

97

Name _____

Matthew learned that he could praise God by singing. Show Matthew his place on the stage. Move one space each time you or your team spell a review word correctly.

F Test-Sentence

The underlined word in this sentence is misspelled. Write the sentence on the

lines below, spelling the underlined word correctly.

It is not kind to <u>het</u> others.

G Test-Words

Write each word as your teacher says it.

1. _____

2. _____

3. _____

4. _____

5. _____

6. _____

7. _____

8. _____

 Test-Challenge Words

Write each challenge word as your teacher says it.

I like praising God
when

Remember: Watch for new ways to
praise God every day!

Spelling Is Fun!

This certificate is awarded to:

_____

for practicing these Spelling words, completing fun activities, and playing great learning games!

_____

Date: _____

an	get	dog	big
man	let	God	dig
ran	bed	on	it
can	red	off	sit
cat	tell	got	hit
at	well	not	did
dad	yes	mom	hid
☆ thank	☆ help	☆ frog	☆ kid
☆ add	☆ best	☆ box	☆ still
☆ ask	☆ next	☆ odd	☆ quit

Dear Parent,

We are about to begin a new Spelling unit containing four weekly lessons. A set of seven words, plus three challenge words, will be studied each week. All the words will be reviewed in the fifth week.

Values, based on each Scripture listed below, will be featured in that week's lesson.

Lesson 6	Lesson 7	Lesson 8	Lesson 9
up	had	in	all
cup	glad	win	ball
bug	am	will	fall
hug	and	if	call
fun	land	him	saw
run	sand	is	law
us	hand	his	jaw
☆ just	☆ plan	☆ finish	☆ small
☆ funny	☆ back	☆ begin	☆ talk
☆ sum	☆ grand	☆ into	☆ draw

Psalm 24:1   Prov. 17:14   Prov. 13:20   Psalm 143:10

A Preview

Write each word as your teacher says it.

Name _____

1. _____

2. _____

3. _____

4. _____

Challenge Words

 _____

5. _____

6. _____
 _____

7. _____
 _____

Scripture

Psalm 24:1

Name _____

Write each word in the correct Word Shape Boxes.
Next, in the Word Shape Boxes, color the letter
that spells the sound of **/u/** in each word.
Circle words that begin with the sound of **/u/**.

1. up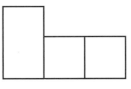

2. cup

3. bug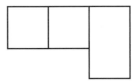

4. hug

5. fun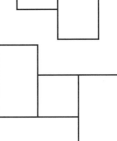

6. run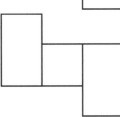

7. us

 Challenge

Draw a Shape Box around each letter:

just   funny   sum

C Hide and Seek

Circle a cookie for each word you spell correctly.

D Other Word Forms

Using the words below, follow instructions given by your teacher.

bugged	funnier	running
bugging	hugged	sums
bugs	hugging	summed
cupped	hugs	we
cups	justly	

E Fun Ways to Spell

Initial the box of each activity you finish.

1.

Spell your words with crayons.

2.

Spell your words with chalk.

3.

Spell your words out loud.

4.

Spell your words in damp sand.

Name _____

Write the missing word in each sentence.

_____

1. I ran _____ the hill.

_____

2. My mom will _____ me.

_____

3. Milk is in my _____.

_____

4. Tom had a _____ in his jar.

_____

5. We had _____ at the park.

_____

6. God wants _____ to care
for the earth.

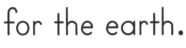

_____

7. Tell him to _____ home.

Word Bank

up	bug	fun	us
cup	hug	run	

G Dictation

Name _____

Listen and write the missing words.

1. ___ is ___ to ___ ___
the park.

2. My ___ and ___
gave me a ___ ___.

3. This ___ ___ fly ___.

H Proofreading

One word in each pair is misspelled.
Fill in the oval by the misspelled word.

1. ◯ up
   ◯ bg

2. ◯ hyg
   ◯ run

3. ◯ fvn
   ◯ cup

4. ◯ bug
   ◯ rin

5. ◯ hug
   ◯ uus

6. ◯ yop
   ◯ fun

☆ ◯ gus
   ◯ kid

☆ ◯ frog
   ◯ funy

☆ ◯ box
   ◯ som

107

I Game

Cross out each **i**, **d**, and **w** with a big **X** to find the hidden spelling words.

Lightly, color the other boxes so you can see your spelling words better.

i	d	w	i	d	b	u	g	w
d	h	u	g	w	i	d	w	i
w	i	f	u	n	n	y	d	w
i	d	w	i	d	f	u	n	w
d	s	u	m	w	i	d	w	i
w	i	d	u	p	w	i	d	w
r	u	n	i	d	w	i	d	w
d	w	i	d	w	i	d	u	s
c	u	p	w	i	d	w	i	d
w	i	d	w	i	j	u	s	t

Remember: Take care of the earth — it belongs to God.

J Journaling

Draw a picture of Mason Springs Park before, during, or after class clean-up day.

A Preview

Write each word as your teacher says it.

Name _____

1. _____

2. _____

3. _____

4. _____

Challenge Words

5. _____

6. _____

7. _____

Scripture

Proverbs 17:14

Write each word in the correct Word Shape Boxes.
Next, in the Word Shape Boxes, color the letter
that spells the sound of /a/ in each word.
Circle words that begin with the sound of /a/.

1. **had**
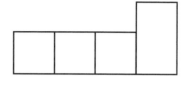

2. **glad**
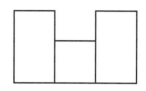

3. **am**
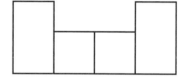

4. **and**

5. **land**
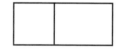

6. **sand**
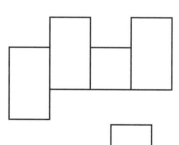

7. **hand**

⭐ **Challenge**
Draw a Shape Box around each letter:

p l a n   b a c k   g r a n d

C Hide and Seek

Circle a cookie for each word you spell correctly.

Name _____

D Other Word Forms

Using the words below, follow instructions given by your teacher.

backs	grandest	have	sanded
backed	hands	landed	sandy
backing	handed	plans	
gladly	handing	planned	
grander	has	planning	

E Fun Ways to Spell

Initial the box of each activity you finish.

1. ☐

Spell your words with puzzles.

3. ☐

Spell your words with rhythm instruments.

2. ☐

Spell your words on the clothesline.

4. ☐

Spell your words with shaving cream.

To find the hidden picture, color the spaces purple that have spelling words in them.

Name _____

Color the spaces red that have challenge words.

Words With /a/

Lesson
7

Word Bank

had	am	land	hand	⭐ back
glad	and	sand	⭐ plan	⭐ grand

112

G Dictation

Name _____

Listen and write the missing words.

1. I _____ _____ we ___ a
_____ _____
_____ _____ .

2. The _____ felt good
___ ___ _____
___ my _____ .

3. I saw the ___ jet _____ .

H Proofreading

One word in each pair is misspelled.
Fill in the oval by the misspelled word.

1. ○ had
   ○ adn

2. ○ sanb
   ○ land

3. ○ glad
   ○ hanb

4. ○ ladn
   ○ and

5. ○ glab
   ○ sand

6. ○ hand
   ○ ama

☆ ○ qlan
  ○ quit

☆ ○ just
  ○ bak

☆ ○ granb
  ○ funny

I Game

Kristin and Cathy learned that it's hard to stop a quarrel once it starts. Kristin asked Cathy to forgive her for breaking her bank and helped her buy a new one. Color one penny for each word you or your team spell correctly from this week's word list.

Remember: Don't quarrel. Arguments are easy to start but hard to stop.

J Journaling

Copy and finish this sentence:
I can keep from quarreling by...

A Preview

Write each word as your teacher says it.

Name _____

1. _____

2. _____

3. _____

4. _____

5. _____

6. _____

7. _____

Challenge Words

☆ _____

☆ _____

☆ _____

Scripture

Proverbs 13:20

Name _____

Write each word in the correct Word Shape Boxes.
Next, in the Word Shape Boxes, color the letter
that spells the sound of **/i/** in each word.
Circle words that begin with the sound of **/i/**.

Words With /i/

Lesson 8

1. in
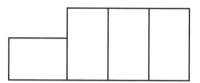

2. win
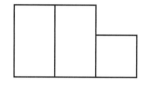

3. will
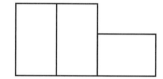

4. if

5. him
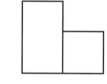

6. is
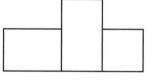

7. his

⭐ **Challenge**

Draw a Shape Box around each letter:

f i n i s h   b e g i n   i n t o

116

C Hide and Seek

Name _____

Circle a cookie for each word you spell correctly.

D Other Word Forms

Using the words below, follow
instructions given by your teacher.

began   willing

finished   winner

finishes   winning

finishing   wins

he   won

E Fun Ways to Spell

Initial the box of each activity you finish.

1. ☐

Spell your words with crayons.

3. ☐

Spell your words from the letter box.

2. ☐

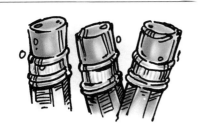

Spell your words with an eraser.

4. ☐

Spell your words with finger paint.

117

F Missing Letters

Add the missing letters to each word.

Name _____

1. h____

2. w____

3. ____s

4. h____

5. ____f

6. ____n

7. w____

⭐ f____ish

Word Bank

in	will	him	his	⭐ begin
win	if	is	⭐ finish	⭐ into

G Dictation

Name _____

Listen and write the missing words.

_____ _____ _____ _____

1. _____ _____ _____ _____●

_____ _____ _____ _____

2. _____ _____ _____ _____

 _the house._

3. _____ _____ I _____

H Proofreading

One word in each pair is misspelled.
Fill in the oval by the misspelled word.

1. ○ wehn   4. ○ him   ☆ ○ finesh
   ○ in   ○ eff   ○ thank

2. ○ if   5. ○ ien   ☆ ○ into
   ○ wil   ○ will   ○ begn

3. ○ hiz   6. ○ heim   ☆ ○ sum
   ○ win   ○ is   ○ nto

I Game

Cross out each **c**, **p**, and **u** with a big **X** to find the hidden spelling words. Using one crayon, softly color the other boxes so you can see your spelling words better.

c	p	u	c	i	f	p	u	c
h	i	m	p	u	c	p	u	c
u	c	p	b	e	g	i	n	u
c	p	u	c	p	u	c	i	n
p	w	i	n	u	c	p	u	c
u	p	c	p	p	c	i	s	u
c	p	h	i	s	u	c	p	u
i	n	t	o	c	p	u	c	p
u	c	f	i	n	i	s	h	p
c	p	u	w	i	l	l	c	p

Remember: Choose friends who love God.

J Journaling

Copy and finish this sentence:
I am being a good friend when I . . .

120

A Preview

Write each word as your teacher says it.

Name _____

1. _____

2. _____

3. _____

4. _____

Challenge Words

5. _____   ⭐ _____

6. _____   ⭐ _____

7. _____   ⭐ _____

Scripture

Psalm 143:10

Name _____

Write each word in the correct Word Shape Boxes.
Next, in the Word Shape Boxes, color the letter or letters
that spell the sound of /ô/ in each word.
Circle words which have double consonants.

1. all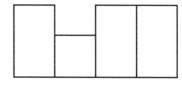

2. ball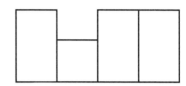

3. fall

4. call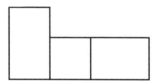

5. saw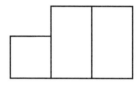

6. law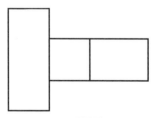

7. jaw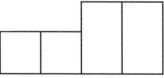

⭐ **Challenge**

Draw a Shape Box around each letter:

s m a l l   t a l k   d r a w

C Hide and Seek

Circle a cookie for each word you spell correctly.

Name _____

D Other Word Forms

Using the words below, follow
instructions given by your teacher.

balls	draws	jaws	smaller
called	drew	lawful	smallest
calling	falling	laws	talked
calls	falls	lawyer	talking
drawing	fell	see	talks

E Fun Ways to Spell

Initial the box of each activity you finish.

1.

Spell your words with puzzles.

3.

Spell your words while clapping.

2.

Spell your words with soap.

4.

Spell your words with play dough.

Name _____

g h k j d
t d r a w
a s a w f
l a w a a
k c a l l
s m a l l

One
secret word
is not used.
Write it here:

_____
- - - - - - - - - - - -
_____

| all | fall | saw | jaw | ☆ talk |
| ball | call | law | ☆ small | ☆ draw |

G Dictation

Listen and write the missing words.

1. The _____ _____ _____ _____ .

2. I obey the _____ of _____ .

3. The _____ _____ _____ _____ .

H Proofreading

One word in each pair is misspelled.
Fill in the oval by the misspelled word.

1. ⬭ oll
   ⬭ his

2. ⬭ dog
   ⬭ lov

3. ⬭ kall
   ⬭ jaw

4. ⬭ law
   ⬭ boll

5. ⬭ sall
   ⬭ all

6. ⬭ call
   ⬭ foll

☆ ⬭ tock
   ⬭ back

☆ ⬭ still
   ⬭ smoll

☆ ⬭ drall
   ⬭ fall

I Game

Name _____

Place a game piece over each word your teacher says and spells. When you get five game pieces in a row, raise your hand and say, "Spelling is fun!"

jaw	in	had	up	cup
all	law	talk	fall	saw
small	glad	FREE	win	if
draw	bug	call	am	will
ball	fun	sand	bug	am

thank	plan	odd	best	all
saw	still	kid	ask	small
talk	fall	FREE	law	call
box	into	add	quit	jaw
back	draw	funny	just	ball

Remember: Ask God to lead you each day.

J Journaling

Copy and finish this sentence:
God helped me to make a good choice when . . .

A Test-Words

Write each word as your teacher says it.

1. _____

2. _____

3. _____

4. _____

5. _____   7. _____

6. _____   8. _____

⭐ Test-Challenge Words

Write each challenge word
as your teacher says it.

Scripture

Proverbs 16:20

In the story from Lesson 6, Rosa learned that the earth belongs to God and that we should take care of it.

Circle one aluminum can for each review word you or your team spell correctly.

RECYCLE

C Test-Sentences

Name _____

The underlined word in each sentence is misspelled. Write the sentences on the lines below, spelling each underlined word correctly.

Can Tommy <u>ron</u>?

1. _____

Daniel put a paper in Tommy's <u>hend</u>.

2. _____

D Test-Proofreading

One word in each pair is misspelled.
Fill in the oval by the misspelled word.

1. ◯ bug
◯ hin

4. ◯ wil
◯ land

7. ◯ his
◯ em

2. ◯ jow
◯ fun

5. ◯ foll
◯ will

8. ◯ lan
◯ fall

3. ◯ am
◯ fn

6. ◯ him
◯ buq

9. ◯ jaw
◯ hiz

 Test-Challenge Words

Write each challenge word as your teacher says it.

129

Name _____

Tommy's mom wanted to make pancakes for him the morning of his math test. Here is her list of things to buy for his favorite breakfast.

Place an **X** by an item each time you or your team spell a review word correctly.

The underlined word in this sentence is misspelled. Write the sentence on the lines below, spelling the underlined word correctly.

Mother said, "Coll your sister."

_____

_____

_____

_____

G **Test-Words**

Write each word as your teacher says it.

1. _____

2. _____

3. _____

4. _____

5. _____

6. _____

7. _____

8. _____

 Test-Challenge Words

Write each challenge word as your teacher says it.

Review

Lesson

10

When I am tempted to cheat I need to

Remember: Trust God and He will bless you.

Spelling Is Fun!

This certificate is awarded to:

_____

- -

_____

for practicing these Spelling words, completing
fun activities, and playing great learning games!

_____

- -

Date: _____

up	had	in	all
cup	glad	win	ball
bug	am	will	fall
hug	and	if	call
fun	land	him	saw
run	sand	is	law
us	hand	his	jaw
☆ just	☆ plan	☆ finish	☆ small
☆ funny	☆ back	☆ begin	☆ talk
☆ sum	☆ grand	☆ into	☆ draw

Dear Parent,

We are about to begin a new Spelling unit containing four weekly lessons. A set of seven words, plus three challenge words, will be studied each week. All the words will be reviewed in the fifth week.

Values, based on each Scripture listed below, will be featured in that week's lesson.

Lesson 11	Lesson 12	Lesson 13	Lesson 14
he	much	may	time
she	but	day	nice
me	cut	away	ice
we	stop	play	wide
see	hop	made	side
feet	top	make	ride
eat	cot	take	hide
☆ each	☆ such	☆ grade	☆ line
☆ he's	☆ clock	☆ pray	☆ write
☆ we'll	☆ drop	☆ came	☆ kind

| Psalm 13:6 | Prov. 14:31 | Prov. 10:22 | Psalm 119:80 |

A Preview

Write each word as your teacher says it.

1. _____

2. _____

3. _____

4. _____

5. _____

6. _____

7. _____

Challenge Words

☆ _____

☆ _____

☆ _____

Scripture

Psalm 13:6

B Word Shapes

Write each word in the correct Word Shape Boxes. Next, in the Word Shape Boxes, color the letter or letters that spell the sound of /ē/ in each word. Circle words that have two vowels together. Draw a line under words that end with the sound of /ē/.

1. he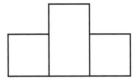

2. she

3. me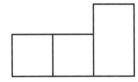

4. we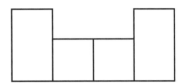

5. see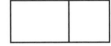

6. feet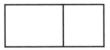

7. eat

 Challenge

Draw a Shape Box around each letter:

  e a c h   h e ' s   w e ' l l

C Hide and Seek

Circle a cookie for each word you spell correctly.

D Other Word Forms

Using the words below, follow instructions given by your teacher.

ate	mine
eating	our
eats	saw
foot	seeing
her	sees

E Fun Ways to Spell

Initial the box of each activity you finish.

1.

Spell your words with crayons.

3.

Spell your words out loud.

2.

Spell your words with sidewalk chalk.

4.

Spell your words in damp sand.

F **Sentence Fun**

Name _____

Write the missing word in the sentence.

1. Come swing with _____ .

2. I _____ the boy.

3. Can _____ play with your doll?

4. _____ like this tree.

5. My _____ got wet in the creek.

6. _____ hit the ball hard.

7. It is time to _____ .

Word Bank			
he	me	see	eat
she	we	feet	

G Dictation

Name _____

Listen and write the missing words.

1. _____ _____ <u>sing</u> <u>songs</u>

<u>to</u> _____ .

2. _____ _____ _____ _____

<u>two</u> _____ _____ <u>this</u> <u>fog.</u>

3. _____ _____ _____ <u>with</u> ___ .

H Proofreading

One word in each pair is misspelled.
Fill in the oval by the misspelled word.

1. ⬭ he   4. ⬭ we   ☆ ⬭ eech
   ⬭ fet   ⬭ sae   ⬭ begin

2. ⬭ shee   5. ⬭ hee   ☆ ⬭ talk
   ⬭ see   ⬭ she   ⬭ wi'll

3. ⬭ eet   6. ⬭ eat   ☆ ⬭ he'z
   ⬭ me   ⬭ mea   ⬭ each

I Game

Cross out each **o**, **k**, and **r** with a big **X** to find the hidden spelling words. Using one

crayon, softly color the other boxes so you can see your spelling words better.

o	k	s	h	e	r	o	k	r
k	r	o	k	r	o	k	h	e
m	e	r	o	k	r	o	k	r
o	k	r	w	e	o	k	r	o
k	r	o	k	r	o	s	e	e
r	o	e	a	c	h	k	r	o
k	r	o	k	r	w	e'	l	l
o	e	a	t	k	r	o	k	r
o	k	r	o	k	f	e	e	t
h	e'	s	r	o	k	r	o	k

Remember: God's blessings often come through people instead of things.

J Journaling

Make a list of some of God's blessings.

A Preview

Write each word as your teacher says it.

Name _____

1. _____

2. _____

3. _____

4. _____

Challenge Words

5. _____   _____

6. _____   _____

7. _____   _____

Scripture

Proverbs 14:31

Write each word in the correct Word Shape Boxes.
Next, in the Word Shape Boxes, color the letter
that spells the sound of /u/ or /o/ in each word.
Circle words that end with the consonant digraph **ch**.

Words with /u/ or /o/

Lesson

12

1. much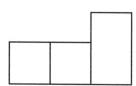

2. but

3. cut

4. stop

5. hop

6. top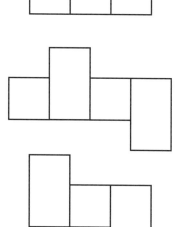

7. cot

 Challenge

Draw a Shape Box around each letter:

s u c h   c l o c k   d r o p

C Hide and Seek

Name _____

Circle a cookie for each word you spell correctly.

D Other Word Forms

Using the words below, follow
instructions given by your teacher.

clocked	dropped	hops	stops
clocks	dropping	many	topped
cots	drops	stopped	topping
cuts	hopped	stopper	tops
cutting	hopping	stopping	

E Fun Ways to Spell

Initial the box of each activity you finish.

1.

Spell your words with puzzles.

3.

Spell your words with rhythm instruments.

2.

Spell your words on the clothesline.

4.

Spell your words with shaving cream.

143

Add the missing letters to each word.

1. m___

2. b___

3. c___

4. st___

5. h___

6. t___

7. c___

⭐ cl___

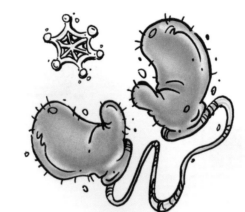

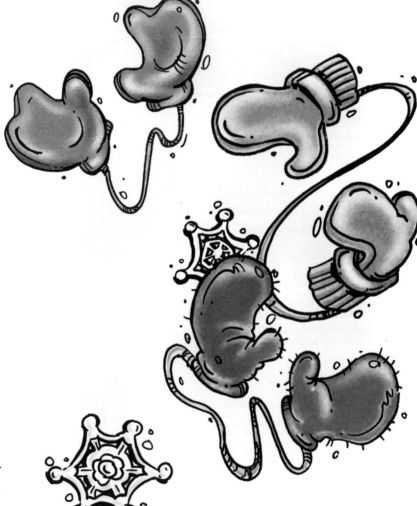

Word Bank

much	cut	hop	cot	⭐ such
but	stop	top	⭐ clock	⭐ drop

G Dictation

Listen and write the missing words.

Name _____

1. _____ _____ _____ _____

   _____

   _____.

2. The _____ _____ _____

   the frog _____.

3. I _____ _____ the _____.

H Proofreading

One word in each pair is misspelled.
Fill in the oval by the misspelled word.

1. ◯ much
   ◯ cawt

2. ◯ toup
   ◯ but

3. ◯ hoq
   ◯ cut

4. ◯ sotp
   ◯ hop

5. ◯ cot
   ◯ cutt

6. ◯ bot
   ◯ top

☆ ◯ clok
   ◯ small

☆ ◯ plan
   ◯ suj

☆ ◯ brop
   ◯ grand

I Game

Name _____

Color one mitten each time you or
your team spell a word correctly.

Remember: Honor God by helping those in need.

J Journaling

Draw a picture of a big snowman. Think of something you
could do to help the poor. Write it on your snowman.

A Preview

Write each word as your teacher says it.

Name _____

1. _____

2. _____

3. _____

4. _____

5. _____

6. _____

7. _____

Challenge Words

 _____

 _____

 _____

Scripture

Proverbs 10:22

Write each word in the correct Word Shape Boxes.
Next, in the Word Shape Boxes, color the letters
that spell the sound of /ā/ in each word.
Circle words that have two syllables.

1. may

2. day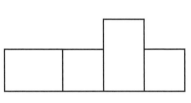

3. away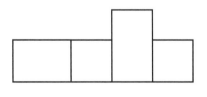

4. play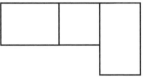

5. made

6. make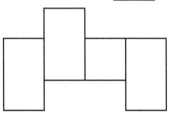

7. take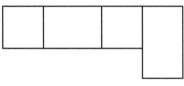

 Challenge

Draw a Shape Box around each letter:

g r a d e   p r a y   c a m e

C Hide and Seek

Circle a cookie for each word you spell correctly.

D Other Word Forms

Using the words below, follow instructions given by your teacher.

come	grades	player	praying
comes	grading	playing	prays
coming	making	plays	takes
days	might	prayed	taking
graded	played	prayer	took

E Fun Ways to Spell

Initial the box of each activity you finish.

1.

Spell your words with crayons.

3.

Spell your words from the letter box.

2.

Spell your words with an eraser.

4.

Spell your words with finger paint.

F ABC Order

Name _____

Write the words from each group in ABC order.

2. day
may

3. made
away

1. play
may

grade
pray
came

4. take
make

1. _____ _____

2. _____ _____

3. _____ _____

4. _____ _____

☆ _____ _____   _____

A B C D E F G H I J K L M N O P Q R S T U V W X Y Z
a b c d e f g h i j k l m n o p q r s t u v w x y z

150

G Dictation

Name _____

Listen and write the missing words.

_____ _____ _____ _____

1. _____ _____ _____ _____

_____

coat.

2. I _____ _____ a lunch

one _____.

3. The _____ _____ _____.

H Proofreading

One word in each pair is misspelled.
Fill in the oval by the misspelled word.

1. ○ maa
   ○ take

2. ○ stop
   ○ plae

3. ○ feet
   ○ uway

4. ○ dae
   ○ saw

5. ○ mak
   ○ made

6. ○ play
   ○ tak

☆ ○ grabe
   ○ came

☆ ○ prae
   ○ draw

☆ ○ finish
   ○ caem

Name _____

Cross out each **i**, **n**, and **s** with a big **X** to find the hidden spelling words. Using one crayon, softly color the boxes you did not mark so you can see your spelling words better.

i	a	w	a	y	n	s	s	i
s	i	i	s	s	n	s	n	n
t	a	k	e	s	i	d	a	y
n	s	i	c	a	m	e	n	s
i	n	s	i	m	a	k	e	n
m	a	y	s	s	n	s	i	i
s	n	n	s	g	r	a	d	e
i	i	p	l	a	y	s	s	n
p	r	a	y	s	n	n	s	i
n	s	s	n	m	a	d	e	s

Remember: Our greatest treasure is God's love.

Copy and finish this thank-you note to God for a blessing He has given you:
Dear God, Thank you for . . .

A Preview

Write each word as your teacher says it.

Name _____

1. _____

2. _____

3. _____

4. _____

5. _____

6. _____

7. _____

Challenge Words

Scripture

Psalm 119:80

Write each word in the correct Word Shape Boxes.
Next, in the Word Shape Boxes, color the letters
that spell the sound of /ī/ in each word.
Circle the silent-**e** in each word.

1. nice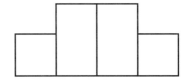

2. ice

3. wide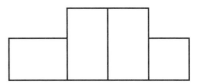

4. side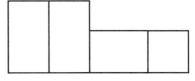

5. ride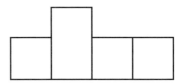

6. hide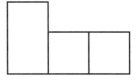

7. time

⭐ **Challenge**

Draw a Shape Box around each letter:

l i n e   w r i t e   k i n d

C Hide and Seek

Circle a cookie for each word you spell correctly.

D Other Word Forms

Using the words below, follow instructions given by your teacher.

hid	kinder	nicest	sided	wider
hidden	kindest	ridden	sides	widest
hides	lined	rider	siding	writes
hiding	lines	rides	timed	written
ices	lining	riding	timer	wrote
icing	nicer	rode	times	

F. Fun Ways to Spell

Initial the box of each activity you finish.

1.

Spell your words with puzzles.

3.

Spell your words while clapping.

2.

Spell your words with soap.

4.

Spell your words with play dough.

```
w  r  i  t  e  s
i  m  k  i  n  d
d  l  o  m  i  v
e  a  s  e  c  b
s  l  i  n  e  d
h  i  d  e  c  e
i  c  e  f  a  b
```

One secret word is not used.

Write it here: _____

Word Bank

nice	wide	ride	time	☆ write
ice	side	hide	☆ line	☆ kind

Words with /ī/

Lesson **14**

G Dictation

Listen and write the missing words.

1. _____ _____ a _____

_____ the _____ rink.

2. _____ _____ go for a _____.

3. The box was too

to fit _____ _____ _____.

H Proofreading

One word in each pair is misspelled.
Fill in the oval by the misspelled word.

1. ○ ride
   ○ ise

2. ○ nice
   ○ wied

3. ○ sibe
   ○ hide

4. ○ tiem
   ○ wide

5. ○ side
   ○ ried

6. ○ nis
   ○ time

☆ ○ lin
   ○ pray

☆ ○ kide
   ○ such

☆ ○ grade
   ○ wriet

I Game

Name _____

Place a game piece over each word your teacher says and spells. When you get five game pieces in a row, raise your hand and say, "Spelling is fun!"

line	he	nice	eat	kind
may	she	ride	day	away
side	write	FREE	time	ice
much	cut	hide	me	take
but	see	wide	cot	top

side	he	much	but	hide
she	time	ice	kind	may
write	stop	FREE	day	take
we	wide	top	ride	hop
nice	play	me	away	line

Remember: Do what's right with a happy heart.

J Journaling

Copy and finish this prayer:
Dear Jesus, Please help . . . .
Ask God to help you do cheerfully, what He wants.

A Test-Words

Write each word as your teacher says it.

1. _____

2. _____

3. _____

4. _____

5. _____

6. _____

7. _____

8. _____

☆ Test-Challenge Words

Write each challenge word
as your teacher says it.

Scripture

Psalm 18:2

In the story from Lesson 13, Rosa and her brother and sister went sledding on the hill behind the Anderson's house. Sled down the hill with Rosa. Color in one space each time you or your team spell a review word correctly.

C Test-Sentences

Name _____

The underlined word in each sentence is misspelled. Write the sentences on the lines below, spelling each underlined word correctly.

What will <u>wi</u> do?

- -

1. _____

We will <u>plae</u> outside in the snow fort.

- -

2. _____

_____

- -

_____

D Test-Proofreading

One word in each pair is misspelled.
Fill in the oval by the misspelled word.

1. ⬭ uway   **4.** ⬭ top   **7.** ⬭ eet
     ⬭ me   ⬭ ct   ⬭ made

2. ⬭ eat   **5.** ⬭ wid   **8.** ⬭ wide
     ⬭ tim   ⬭ cot   ⬭ toq

3. ⬭ mee   **6.** ⬭ away   **9.** ⬭ kot
     ⬭ cut   ⬭ mabe   ⬭ time

☆ Test-Challenge Words

Write each challenge word as your teacher says it.

E **Game**

Name _____

Matthew and Emily got separated from their mom in the grocery store. Show Matthew the way to the friendly store clerk, who will help him and Emily find their mom. Move one space each time you or your team spell a review word correctly.

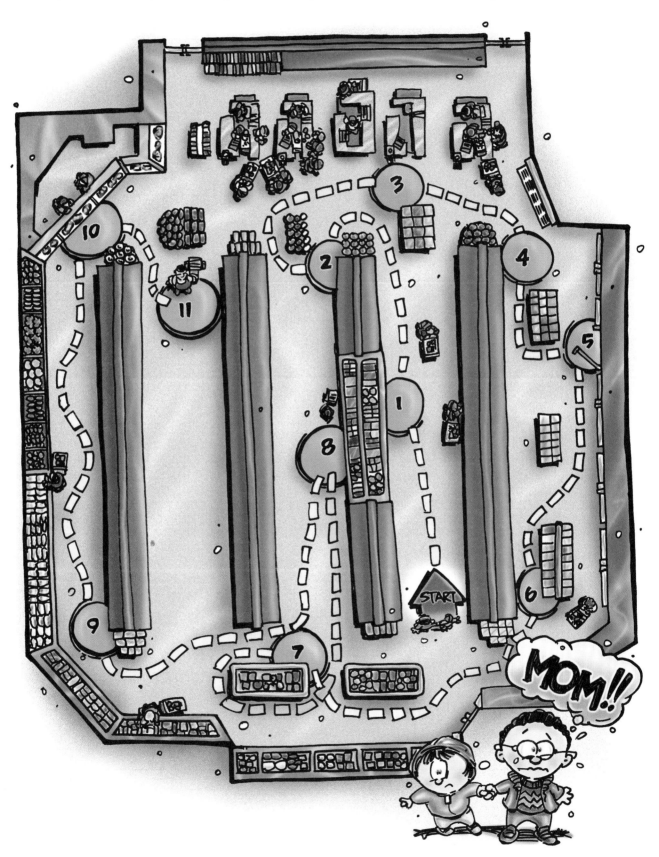

F Test-Sentence

Name _____

The underlined word in each sentence is misspelled. Write the sentences on the lines below, spelling each underlined word correctly.

We will <u>hibe</u> in the snow fort.

_____

- - - - - - - - - - - - - - - - - -

_____

_____

- - - - - - - - - - - - - - - - - -

_____

G Test-Words

Write each word as your teacher says it.

1. _____

2. _____

3. _____

4. _____

5. _____

6. _____

7. _____

8. _____

 Test-Challenge Words

Write each challenge word as your teacher says it.

Review

Lesson
15

I feel like I need
a safe fort when

_____

- - - - - - - - - - - - - - -

_____

_____

- - - - - - - - - - - - - - -

_____

_____

- - - - - - - - - - - - - - -

_____

Remember: When you are afraid,
call on Jesus.

Spelling Is Fun!

This certificate is awarded to:

_____

- - - - - - - - - - - - - - - - -

_____

for practicing these Spelling words, completing
fun activities, and playing great learning games!

_____

- - - - - - - - - - - - - - - - -

Date: _____

he	much	may	time
she	but	day	nice
me	cut	away	ice
we	stop	play	wide
see	hop	made	side
feet	top	make	ride
eat	cot	take	hide
☆ each	☆ such	☆ grade	☆ line
☆ he's	☆ clock	☆ pray	☆ write
☆ we'll	☆ drop	☆ came	☆ kind

Dear Parent,

We are about to begin a new Spelling unit containing four weekly lessons. A set of seven words, plus three challenge words, will be studied each week. All the words will be reviewed in the fifth week.

Values, based on each Scripture listed below, will be featured in that week's lesson.

Lesson 16	Lesson 17	Lesson 18	Lesson 19
my	when	they	now
by	then	them	how
try	hen	there	down
why	ten	this	town
no	went	the	our
so	send	with	out
go	cent	thing	about
☆ going	☆ pencil	☆ than	☆ vowel
☆ most	☆ penny	☆ these	☆ south
☆ know	☆ sentence	☆ think	☆ round

Prov. 3:3	Psalm 119:33, 35	Prov. 17:17	Psalm 5:11

A Preview

Write each word as your teacher says it.

Name _____

1. _____

2. _____

3. _____

4. _____

5. _____

6. _____

7. _____

Challenge Words

_____

_____

_____

Scripture

Proverbs 3:3

Name _____

Write each word in the correct Word Shape Boxes.
Next, in the Word Shape Boxes, color the letter
that spells the sound of /ī/ or /ō/ in each word.
Circle words that begin with the digraph **wh**.

1. my

2. by

3. try

4. why

5. no

6. so

7. go

☆ **Challenge**
Draw a Shape Box around each letter:

going   most   know

C Hide and Seek

Name ______________________________

Circle a cookie for each word you spell correctly.

D Other Word Forms

Using the words below, follow instructions given by your teacher.

goes	mine
going	tried
knew	tries
knows	trying

E Fun Ways to Spell

Initial the box of each activity you finish.

1.

Spell your words with crayons.

2.

Spell your words with chalk.

3.

Spell your words out loud.

4.

Spell your words in damp sand.

Write the missing word in each sentence.

1. We want to _____ with you.

2. Please let me _____ to do it.

3. Your bike is _____ my bike.

4. This is _____ friend.

5. I always ask _____.

6. It snowed _____ much, we went sledding.

7. It is _____ fun to be cold.

Word Bank

my	try	no	go
by	why	so	

G Dictation

Name _____

Listen and write the missing words.

1. I _____ _____ to _____.

2. _____ _____ _____ _____ _____

fast?

3. _____, _____ _____ _____

_____ _____

_____ _____.

H Proofreading

One word in each pair is misspelled.
Fill in the oval by the misspelled word.

1. ○ try
   ○ hwy

2. ○ my
   ○ soe

3. ○ no
   ○ bi

4. ○ trie
   ○ go

5. ○ by
   ○ goi

6. ○ why
   ○ mie

☆ ○ mosk
  ○ kind

☆ ○ pray
  ○ gowing

☆ ○ clock
  ○ kno

171

I Game

Cross out each **e**, **q**, and **z** with a big **X** to find the hidden spelling words. Using one crayon, softly color the boxes you did not mark so you can see your spelling words better.

e	q	z	e	q	z	e	b	y
q	w	h	y	z	e	q	z	e
q	z	e	q	z	e	q	n	o
g	o	z	e	q	z	e	q	z
e	q	z	e	m	y	q	z	e
q	k	n	o	w	z	e	q	z
t	r	y	e	q	z	e	s	o
q	z	e	q	z	e	q	z	e
z	e	q	g	o	i	n	g	z
m	o	s	t	e	q	z	e	q

Remember: Be kind and truthful, even if it's not easy.

J Journaling

Draw a picture of Beth taking Luke's tube.
Label the picture **A Bad Choice**. Draw Beth giving Luke's tube back. Label it **A Good Choice**.

A Preview

Write each word as your teacher says it.

Name _____

1. _____

2. _____

3. _____

4. _____

5. _____

6. _____

7. _____

Challenge Words

_____

_____

_____

Scripture

Psalm 119:33, 35

B **Word Shapes**

Write each word in the correct Word Shape Boxes.
Next, in the Word Shape Boxes, color the
letters **en** in each word. Circle the words
that begin with a digraph.

1. when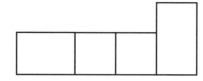

2. then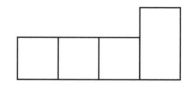

3. hen

4. ten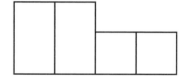

5. went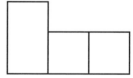

6. send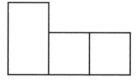

7. cent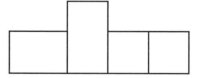

⭐ **Challenge**

Draw a Shape Box around each letter:

p e n c i l   p e n n y   s e n t e n c e

174

C Hide and Seek

Circle a cookie for each word you spell correctly.

D Other Word Forms

Using the words below, follow instructions given by your teacher.

cents	pennies
hens	sending
penciled	sends
penciling	sent
pencils	sentences

E Fun Ways to Spell

Initial the box of each activity you finish.

1.

Spell your words with puzzles.

3.

Spell your words with rhythm instruments.

2.

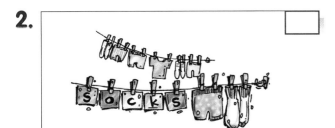

Spell your words on the clothesline.

4.

Spell your words with shaving cream.

Write the words from each group
in ABC order.

2. went

send

3. when

then

4. send

cent

1. hen

ten

_____ _____

1. _____ _____

_____ _____

2. _____ _____

_____ _____

3. _____ _____

_____ _____

4. _____ _____

☆ pencil

penny

sentence

_____ _____ _____

☆ _____ _____ _____

A B C D E F G H I J K L M N O P Q R S T U V W X Y Z
a b c d e f g h i j k l m n o p q r s t u v w x y z

G Dictation

Name _____

Listen and write the missing words.

1. _____ have _____ _____ .

2. _____ _____ home,

_____ came back.

3. _____ the letter

_____ you _____ .

H Proofreading

One word in each pair is misspelled.
Fill in the oval by the misspelled word.

1. ○ hin
   ○ ice

2. ○ wint
   ○ when

3. ○ senb
   ○ ten

4. ○ then
   ○ cint

5. ○ went
   ○ tein

6. ○ cent
   ○ hwen

☆ ○ pene
   ○ line

☆ ○ pensle
   ○ know

☆ ○ write
   ○ sintins

177

I Game

As he was eating tacos for dinner, Tommy's dad assured him that God would guide him in his decisions. Color one tomato piece each time you or your team spell a word correctly from this week's word list.

Remember: Ask God what to do, then do it!

J Journaling

Copy and finish these sentences:
I am telling when I . . .
I am tattling when I . . .

A Preview

Write each word as your teacher says it.

Name _____

1. _____

2. _____

3. _____

4. _____

5. _____

6. _____

7. _____

Challenge Words

 _____

 _____

 _____

Scripture

Proverbs 17:17

B **Word Shapes**

Name _____

Write each word in the correct Word Shape Boxes.
Next, in the Word Shape Boxes, color the letters
that spell the sound of /**th**/ or /**th**/ in each word.
Circle the words in which you use your voice
to say the sound of /**th**/.

1. they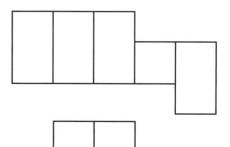

2. them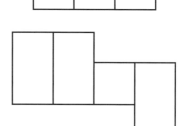

3. there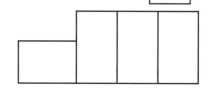

4. this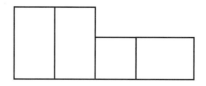

5. the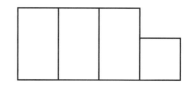

6. with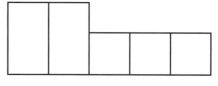

7. thing

☆ **Challenge**

Draw a Shape Box around each letter:

than   these   think

180

C Hide and Seek

Circle a cookie for each word you spell correctly.

D Other Word Forms

Using the words below, follow instructions given by your teacher.

their	thinking
theirs	thinks
things	thought

F Fun Ways to Spell

Initial the box of each activity you finish.

1.

Spell your words with crayons.

3.

Spell your words from the letter box.

2.

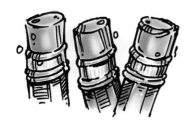

Spell your words with an eraser.

4.

Spell your words with finger paint.

181

F **Word Scramble**

Name _____

Unscramble the letters to make a spelling word.

1. _____

2. _____

3. _____

4. _____

5. _____

6. _____

7. _____

⭐ _____

⭐ _____

⭐ _____

1. het

2. isth

3. tihw

4. yeth

5. hemt

6. heert

7. gnhti

⭐ hant

⭐ teesh

⭐ kinth

Word Bank

they	there	the	thing	⭐ these
them	this	with	⭐ than	⭐ think

G Dictation

Name _____

Listen **and** write the missing words.

1. _____ _____ _____

_____ _____ 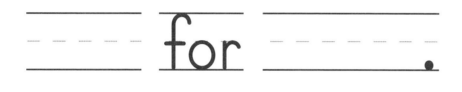 morning.

2. I hope _____ _____

_____ for _____.

3. _____ _____ _____ _____.

H Proofreading

One word in each pair is misspelled.
Fill in the oval by the misspelled word.

1. ○ theng
   ○ send

2. ○ weth
   ○ hen

3. ○ them
   ○ thay

4. ○ this
   ○ thar

5. ○ the
   ○ thim

6. ○ thing
   ○ thes

☆ ○ the
   ○ thna

☆ ○ thenk
   ○ pencil

☆ ○ penny
   ○ thez

I Game

Name _____

Cross out each **b**, **f**, and **z** with a big **X** to find the hidden spelling words. Using one crayon, softly color the boxes you did not mark so you can see your spelling words better.

t	h	e	b	t	h	e	s	e
f	f	t	h	i	s	z	b	f
b	z	z	b	f	t	h	e	m
z	f	b	t	h	e	y	f	z
f	b	b	z	f	z	f	b	z
z	z	t	h	i	n	g	f	f
b	f	z	b	f	w	i	t	h
f	t	h	i	n	k	z	b	f
z	z	z	f	b	t	h	a	n
t	h	e	r	e	b	b	z	f

Remember: Through our friends, God helps us.

J Journaling

Copy and finish this sentence:
I can be a true friend by . . .
Write three ways to be a good friend.

A Preview

Write each word as your teacher says it.

Name _____

1. _____

2. _____

3. _____

4. _____

5. _____

6. _____

7. _____

Challenge Words

⭐ _____

⭐ _____

⭐ _____

Scripture

Psalm 5:11

Write each word in the correct Word Shape Boxes.
Next, in the Word Shape Boxes, color the letters
that spell the sound of **/ou/** in each word.
Circle words that have two syllables.

1. now

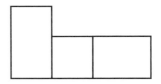

2. how

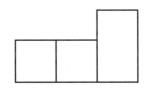

3. down

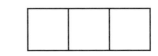

4. town

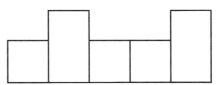

5. our

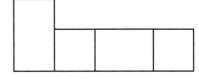

6. out

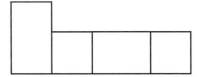

7. about

 Challenge

Draw a Shape Box around each letter:

v o w e l   s o u t h   r o u n d

C Hide and Seek

Name _____

Circle a cookie for each word you spell correctly.

D Other Word Forms

Using the words below, follow instructions given by your teacher.

ours	rounding
outing	rounds
rounded	towns
rounder	vowels

E Fun Ways to Spell

Initial the box of each activity you finish.

1.

Spell your words with puzzles.

3.

Spell your words while clapping.

2.

Spell your words with soap.

4.

Spell your words with play dough.

F Missing Letters

Name _____

Write the word on the line.
Add the missing letters to each word.

1. t __ n

2. __ r

3. n __

4. __ t

5. d __ n

6. ab __ t

7. h __

⭐ s __ th

⭐ r __ nd

⭐ v __ el

Word Bank

now	down	our	about	⭐ south
how	town	out	⭐ vowel	⭐ round

G Dictation

Name _____

Listen and write the missing words.

1. _____ _____ _____ _____

to _____ _____ _____ ?

2. _____ _____ _____ _____

_____ _____ ?

3. _____ _____ _____ _____ .

H Proofreading

One word in each pair is misspelled.
Fill in the oval by the misspelled word.

1. ◯ so
   ◯ owt

2. ◯ they
   ◯ toun

3. ◯ owr
   ◯ now

4. ◯ how
   ◯ ubot

5. ◯ nou
   ◯ out

6. ◯ doun
   ◯ our

☆ ◯ sath
   ◯ these

☆ ◯ think
   ◯ rownd

☆ ◯ vawel
   ◯ about

I Game

Place a game piece over each word your teacher says and spells. When you get five

game pieces in a row, raise your hand and say, "Spelling is fun!"

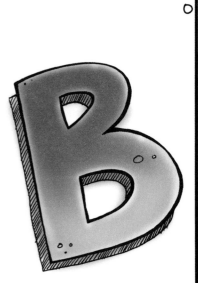

A

round	they	town	go	now
cent	hen	than	south	no
most	so	FREE them		these
know	how	think	went	why
vowel	down	our	about	out

B

how	my	penny	now	ten
vowel	there	by	send	this
our	the	FREE pencil		with
round	going	thing	than	try
down	out	about	town	south

Remember: Let God fill you with His joy!

J Journaling

Draw a picture of something you could do that would create joy.
Label your picture: **God's Kind of Happiness**.

A Test-Words

Name _____

Write each word as your teacher says it.

1. _____

2. _____

3. _____

4. _____

5. _____ 7. _____

6. _____ 8. _____

☆ Test-Challenge Words

Write each challenge word
as your teacher says it.

Scripture

Psalm 40:8

Name _____

In the story from Lesson 19, Tony learned that God can fill his heart with happiness even when it's cloudy and rainy outside.

Color one sun each time you or your team spell a review word correctly.

C Test-Sentences

The underlined word in each sentence is misspelled. Write the sentences on the lines below, spelling each underlined word correctly.

Stephen stole <u>teh</u> gum.

1. _____

I would like <u>tin</u> pieces of bubble gum.

2. _____

D Test-Proofreading

One word in each pair is misspelled.
Fill in the oval by the misspelled word.

1. ○ try
　　○ doun

2. ○ sint
　　○ why

3. ○ htis
　　○ go

4. ○ hen
　　○ ubout

5. ○ cent
　　○ hin

6. ○ them
　　○ tri

7. ○ goe
　　○ this

8. ○ thim
　　○ down

9. ○ about
　　○ wy

 Test-Challenge Words

Write each challenge word
as your teacher says it.

Stephen needs to pay for the piece of gum that he took. Lead the way to the grocery store by moving one space each time you or your team spell a review word correctly.

F Test-Sentence

The underlined word in this sentence is misspelled. Write the sentence on the lines below, spelling the underlined word correctly.

Stephen went to <u>twon</u> to pay for the gum.

_____

_____

_____

_____

_____

G Test-Words

Write each word as your teacher says it.

1. _____

2. _____

3. _____

4. _____

5. _____

6. _____

7. _____

8. _____

 Test-Challenge Words

Write each challenge word as your teacher says it.

195

H Writing Assessment

Name _____

Inside the heart draw a picture of
Stephen and his dad studying God's rules.
Write a sentence about God's rules.

Remember: God's laws make life
easier and better!

Spelling Is Fun!

This certificate is awarded to:

_____

- - - - - - - - - - - - - - - - - -

_____

for practicing these Spelling words, completing
fun activities, and playing great learning games!

_____

- - - - - - - - - - - - - - - - - -

Date: _____

my	when	they	now
by	then	them	how
try	hen	there	down
why	ten	this	town
no	went	the	our
so	send	with	out
go	cent	thing	about
☆ going	☆ pencil	☆ than	☆ vowel
☆ most	☆ penny	☆ these	☆ south
☆ know	☆ sentence	☆ think	☆ round

Dear Parent,

We are about to begin a new Spelling unit containing four weekly lessons. A set of seven words, plus three challenge words, will be studied each week. All the words will be reviewed in the fifth week.

Values, based on each Scripture listed below, will be featured in that week's lesson.

Lesson 21	Lesson 22	Lesson 23	Lesson 24
do	boy	as	mother
to	joy	has	her
you	some	that	girl
school	come	happy	your
good	from	after	or
look	love	was	for
put	of	said	are
☆ tooth	☆ enjoy	☆ have	☆ Lord
☆ books	☆ above	☆ hasn't	☆ first
☆ soon	☆ none	☆ wasn't	☆ circle

Psalm 28:7   Psalm 119:73   Prov. 3:6   Prov. 29:18

A Preview

Write each word as your teacher says it.

Name _____

1. _____

2. _____

3. _____

4. _____

Challenge Words

5. _____

6. _____

7. _____

Scripture

Psalm 28:7

Write each word in the correct Word Shape Boxes.
Next, in the Word Shape Boxes, color the letter
or letters that spell the sound of /ů/, /ü/, or /ū/
in each word. Circle words that are spelled with **oo**.

Words with /ů/, /ü/, or /ū/

Lesson **21**

1. do

2. to

3. you

4. school

5. good

6. look

7. put

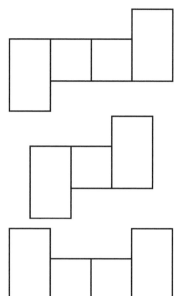
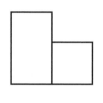

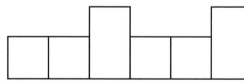

⭐ **Challenge**

Draw a Shape Box around each letter:

t o o t h   b o o k s   s o o n

C Hide and Seek

Circle a cookie for each word you spell correctly.

Name _____

D Other Word Forms

Using the words below, follow instructions given by your teacher.

book	did	putting	teeth
booked	done	schooling	teething
booking	looked	schools	your
does	looking	sooner	
doing	puts	soonest	

E Fun Ways to Spell

Initial the box of each activity you finish.

1.

Spell your words with crayons.

3.

Spell your words out loud.

2.

Spell your words with sidewalk chalk.

4.

Spell your words in damp sand.

201

F **Missing Letters**

Name _____

Add the missing letters to each word.

b __ __ ks

1. t __ __

2. sch __ __ l

3. g __ __ d

__ s __ __ n

4. __ __ __ k

5. d __

6. y __ __

7. p __ t

__ t __ __ th

Word Bank

do	you	good	put	⭐ books
to	school	look	⭐ tooth	⭐ soon

202

G Dictation

Name _____

Listen and write the missing words.

1. _____ _____ _____ _____ ?

2. _____ _____ _____ _____

3. _____ your books

H Proofreading

One word in each pair is misspelled.
Fill in the oval by the misspelled word.

1. ⬭ yuw
   ⬭ put

2. ⬭ skool
   ⬭ good

3. ⬭ look
   ⬭ tuo

4. ⬭ town
   ⬭ luuk

5. ⬭ school
   ⬭ guud

6. ⬭ down
   ⬭ dou

☆ ⬭ sune
   ⬭ south

☆ ⬭ tuth
   ⬭ with

☆ ⬭ most
   ⬭ bux

I Game

Name _____

Tony got a new race track and cars from his papa. Choose one of the cars at the starting line to race. Color in one section of the race track in front of that car for each word you or your team spell correctly from this week's word list.

Remember: When things go wrong,
find something to be joyful about.

J Journaling

Make a list of what makes you feel happy or times you feel like singing. Label the list.

A Preview

Write each word as your teacher says it.

1. _____

2. _____

3. _____

4. _____

5. _____

6. _____

7. _____

Challenge Words

 _____

 _____

 _____

Scripture

Psalm 119:73

Write each word in the correct Word Shape Boxes.
Next, in the Word Shape Boxes, color the letter or
letters that spell the sound of **/oi/** or **/u/** in
each word. Circle words that end with silent-**e**.

1. boy

2. joy

3. some

4. come

5. from

6. love

7. of

⭐ **Challenge**
Draw a Shape Box around each letter:

enjoy   above   none

C Hide and Seek

Name _____

Circle a cookie for each word you spell correctly.

D Other Word Forms

Using the words below, follow instructions given by your teacher.

boys	enjoyed	loved
came	enjoying	lovely
comes	joyful	loves
coming	joys	loving

E Fun Ways to Spell

Initial the box of each activity you finish.

1. ☐

Spell your words with puzzles.

3. ☐

Spell your words with rhythm instruments.

2. ☐

Spell your words on the clothesline.

4. ☐

Spell your words with shaving cream.

Color each spelling word. Trace the path from start to finish.

Start

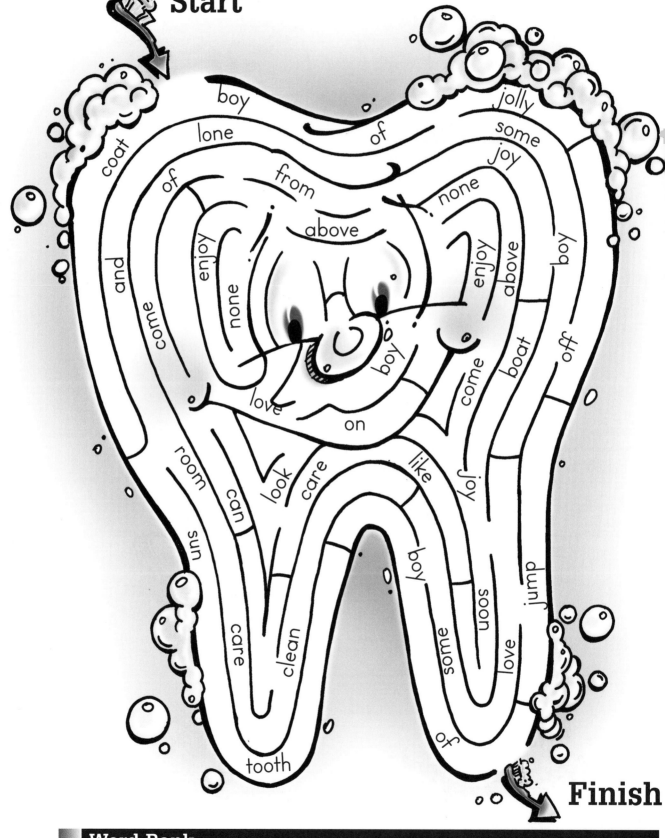

boy
of
jolly
some
lone
coat
joy
of
from
none
above
enjoy
above
and
enjoy
boy
none
come
come
boat
off
love
boy
on
like
joy
room
can
look
care
sun
care
clean
boy
some
soon
love
jump
tooth
of

Finish

Words with /oi/ or /u/

Lesson
22

Word Bank

boy	some	from	of	☆ above
joy	come	love	☆ enjoy	☆ none

G Dictation

Listen and write the missing words.

Name _____

1. _____ _____ _____ a box

_____ _____ new toys.

2. _____ _____ _____ _____

_____ _____

_____ _____ .

3. I _____ _____ raisins.

H Proofreading

One word in each pair is misspelled.
Fill in the oval by the misspelled word.

1. ○ boy
   ○ jowe

2. ○ from
   ○ som

3. ○ lov
   ○ of

4. ○ frum
   ○ come

5. ○ love
   ○ ov

6. ○ some
   ○ bowe

☆ ○ abuv
   ○ round

☆ ○ books
   ○ injoy

☆ ○ nune
   ○ you

209

I Game

Help Tommy take care of his teeth. Color in one blob of toothpaste on a toothbrush for each word you or your team spell correctly from this week's word list.

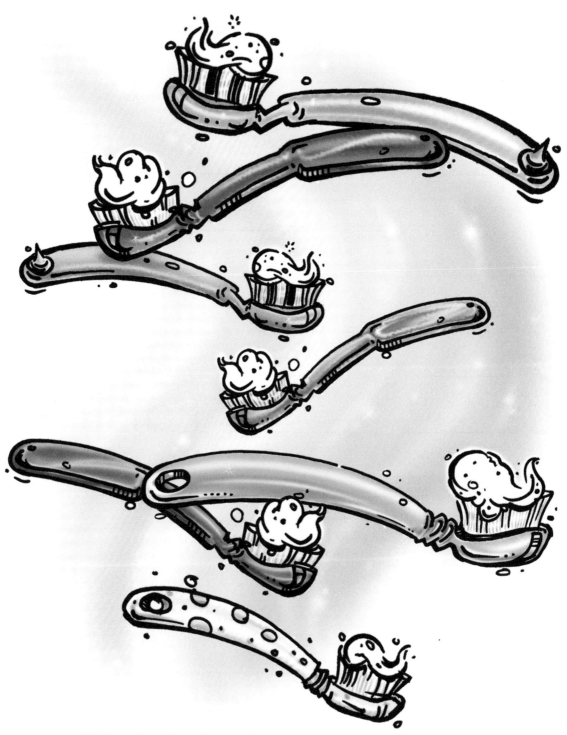

Remember: Follow God's rules and take care of your body.

J Journaling

Copy this sentence in your journal:
I will take care of the body God made for me.
Make a list of at least six of the laws of health.

A Preview

Write each word as your teacher says it.

Name _____

1. _____

2. _____

3. _____

4. _____

5. _____

6. _____

7. _____

Challenge Words

Scripture

Proverbs 3:6

B Word Shapes

Name _____

Write each word in the correct Word Shape Boxes.
Next, in the word Boxes, color the letter
that spells the sound of /a/ in each word,
except **was** and **said**. Circle words in which
the letter **a** has the sound of /u/ or /e/.

1. as

2. has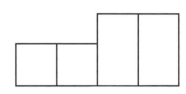

3. that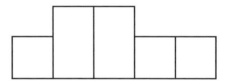

4. happy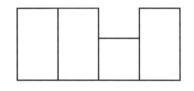

5. after

6. was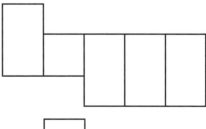

7. said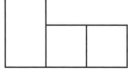

☆ **Challenge**

Draw a Shape Box around each letter:

h a v e   h a s n ' t   w a s n ' t

C Hide and Seek

Name _____

Circle a cookie for each word you spell correctly.

D Other Word Forms

Using the words below, follow
instructions given by your teacher.

happier	had	says
happiest	having	those
happily	say	were
happiness	saying	

E Fun Ways to Spell

Initial the box of each activity you finish.

1.

Spell your words with crayons.

3.

Spell your words from the letter box.

2.

Spell your words with an eraser.

4.

Spell your words with finger paint.

213

F **Word Scramble**

Name _____

Unscramble the letters to make a spelling word.
Write the word on the line.

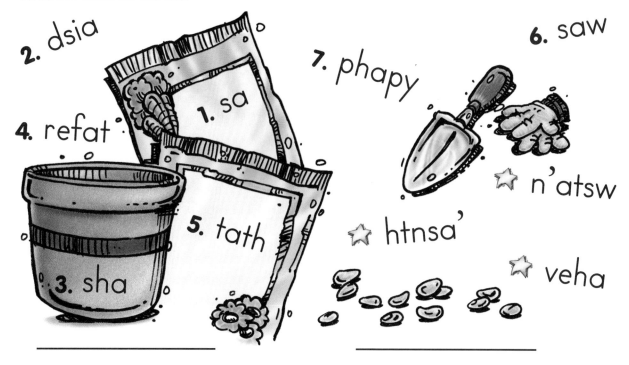

2. dsia

6. saw

7. phapy

1. sa

4. refat

⭐ n'atsw

5. tath

⭐ htnsa'

3. sha

⭐ veha

1. _____

6. _____

2. _____

7. _____

3. _____

⭐ _____

4. _____

⭐ _____

5. _____

⭐ _____

Word Bank

| as | that | after | said | ⭐ hasn't |
| has | happy | was | ⭐ have | ⭐ wasn't |

G Dictation

Name _____

Listen and write the missing words.

1. Are _____ _____ _____

_____ I _____ ?

2. _____ _____ _____ _____

going _____ lunch.

3. _____ _____ a _____ _____ .

H Proofreading

One word in each pair is misspelled.
Fill in the oval by the misspelled word.

1. ⭕ hapy
   ⭕ said

2. ⭕ has
   ⭕ aftr

3. ⭕ as
   ⭕ wuz

4. ⭕ sed
   ⭕ that

5. ⭕ haz
   ⭕ happy

6. ⭕ after
   ⭕ thet

☆ ⭕ wuzn't
   ⭕ vowel

☆ ⭕ above
   ⭕ hazn't

☆ ⭕ soon
   ⭕ hav

I Game

Name _____

Cross out each **c**, **k**, and **o** with a big **X** to find the hidden spelling words. Using one crayon, softly color the boxes you did not mark so you can see your spelling words better.

c	k	h	a	s	n'	t	o	c
c	k	k	o	t	h	a	t	o
a	s	c	o	o	c	k	c	c
o	k	o	c	s	a	i	d	k
k	h	a	s	k	c	c	k	k
o	c	k	o	h	a	v	e	o
c	o	o	h	a	p	p	y	c
k	w	a	s	n'	t	k	c	o
a	f	t	e	r	c	c	o	k
o	o	c	k	k	c	w	a	s

Remember: Always put God first in everything!

J Journaling

List several ways you can put others first.
(Remember the Good Samaritan in the Bible.)

A Preview

Write each word as your teacher says it.

1. _____

2. _____

3. _____

4. _____

5. _____

6. _____

7. _____

Challenge Words

_____

_____

_____

Scripture

Proverbs 29:18

B **Word Shapes**

Name _____

Write each word in the correct Word Shape Boxes.
Next, in the word Boxes, color the letter **r**
and the vowel or vowels that come before **r**
to give the **r**-controlled vowel sound.
Circle words that contains a digraph.

1. mother

2. her

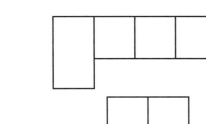

3. girl

4. your

5. or

6. for

7. are

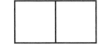

⭐ **Challenge**

Draw a Shape Box around each letter:

Lord   first   circle

C Hide and Seek

Circle a cookie for each word you spell correctly.

D Other Word Forms

Using the words below, follow
instructions given by your teacher.

circled	mothered	yourself
circles	mothering	
circling	mothers	
girls	yours	

E Fun Ways to Spell

Initial the box of each activity you finish.

1.

Spell your words with puzzles.

3.

Spell your words while clapping.

2.

Spell your words with soap.

4.

Spell your words with play dough.

F **Word Maze**

Name _____

Color each spelling word from the
Word Bank. Then, Trace the path

of your colored words from
start to finish.

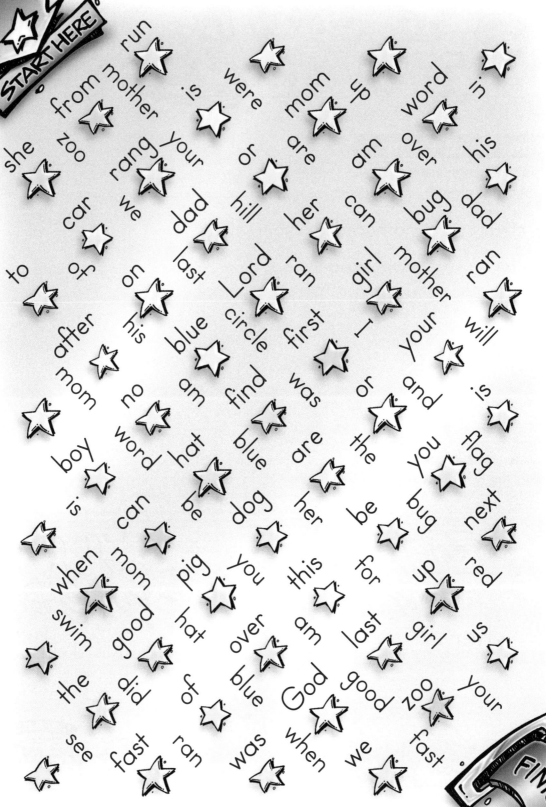

Word Bank

mother	girl	or	are	☆ first	
her	your	for	☆ Lord	☆ circle	

G Dictation

Listen and write the missing words.

1. _____ _____ _____ like

2. _____ _____ _____ _____ _____

_____ ?

3. _____ _____ _____ _____

H Proofreading

One word in each pair is misspelled.
Fill in the oval by the misspelled word.

1. ○ arr
   ○ her

2. ○ girl
   ○ farr

3. ○ your
   ○ hur

4. ○ muthr
   ○ are

5. ○ yur
   ○ for

6. ○ are
   ○ orr

☆ ○ ferst
   ○ hasn't

☆ ○ Lord
   ○ surkl

☆ ○ tooth
   ○ lored

I Game

Place a game piece over each word your teacher says and spells. When you get five game pieces in a row, raise your hand and say, "Spelling is fun!"

was	her	of	to	look
come	Lord	some	said	your
love	for	FREE	good	as
school	circle	has	you	put
mother	or	girl	first	are

mother	after	come	boy	for
good	your	that	girl	joy
do	to	FREE	you	or
look	are	some	first	was
Lord	said	circle	after	her

Remember: Honor God by obeying His laws and the laws of our country.

J Journaling

Write one way you have obeyed God's laws by obeying a law of our country.

A Test-Words

Write each word as your teacher says it.

1. _____

2. _____

3. _____

4. _____

5. _____

6. _____

7. _____

8. _____

☆ Test-Challenge Words

Write each challenge word
as your teacher says it.

Scripture

Proverbs 16:24

B Game

In the story from Lesson 24, Christopher learned that we obey God by obeying the laws of our country. Color one star for each review word you or your team spell correctly.

C **Test-Sentences**

Name _____

The underlined word in each sentence is misspelled. Write the sentences on the lines below, spelling each underlined word correctly.

Rosa <u>sed</u>, "Hello."

1. _____

God wants us to <u>luv</u> one another.

2. _____

_____

D **Test-Proofreading**

One word in each pair is misspelled.
Fill in the oval by the misspelled word.

1. ⬭ gurl
⬭ you

4. ⬭ some
⬭ ar

7. ⬭ was
⬭ uf

2. ⬭ look
⬭ sume

5. ⬭ of
⬭ luk

8. ⬭ girl
⬭ pt

3. ⬭ htat
⬭ put

6. ⬭ yu
⬭ that

9. ⬭ wuz
⬭ are

 Test-Challenge Words

Write each challenge word as your teacher says it.

E Game

Rosa's kind words helped Rachel feel welcome on her first day at school. Lead Rachel to the playground to jump rope with

Rosa by moving one space each time you or your team spell a review word correctly.

F Test-Sentence

The underlined word in this sentence is misspelled. Write the sentence on the lines below, spelling the underlined word correctly.

This is <u>yor</u> new home.

_____

- -

_____

_____

- -

_____

Review

Lesson

25

G Test-Words

Write each word as your teacher says it.

_____

- -

1. _____

5. _____

- -

_____

- -

2. _____

6. _____

- -

_____

- -

3. _____

7. _____

- -

_____

- -

4. _____

8. _____

 Test-Challenge Words

Write each challenge word as your teacher says it.

Design a sign that reminds people to use kind words. Use words and pictures.

Remember: Saying kind things to someone is like giving them delicious food to eat!

Spelling Is Fun!

This certificate is awarded to:

_____

_ _ _ _ _ _ _ _ _ _ _ _ _ _ _ _ _ _

_____

for practicing these Spelling words, completing
fun activities, and playing great learning games!

_____

_ _ _ _ _ _ _ _ _ _ _ _ _ _ _ _ _ _

Date: _____

do	boy	as	mother
to	joy	has	her
you	some	that	girl
school	come	happy	your
good	from	after	or
look	love	was	for
put	of	said	are
☆ tooth	☆ enjoy	☆ have	☆ Lord
☆ books	☆ above	☆ hasn't	☆ first
☆ soon	☆ none	☆ wasn't	☆ circle

Dear Parent,

We are about to begin the last Spelling unit containing three weekly lessons. A set of seven words, plus three challenge words, will be studied each week. All the words will be reviewed in the final week.

Values, based on each Scripture listed below, will be featured in that week's lesson.

Lesson 26	Lesson 27	Lesson 28
one	blue	little
two	black	tall
three	brown	short
four	green	long
five	yellow	few
six	white	many
seven	pink	more
☆ zero	☆ orange	☆ thin
☆ count	☆ purple	☆ thick
☆ number	☆ color	☆ digit

Psalm 96:1, 2   Prov. 14:14   Prov. 10:4

A Preview

Write each word as your teacher says it.

Name _____

1. _____

2. _____

3. _____

4. _____

5. _____

6. _____

7. _____

Challenge Words

_____

_____

_____

Scripture

Psalm 96:1, 2

Write each word in the correct Word Shape Boxes.

 **Number Words**

Lesson **26**

1. one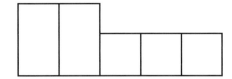

2. two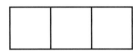

3. three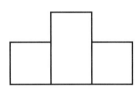

4. four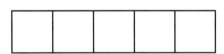

5. five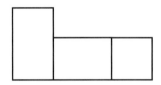

6. six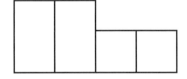

7. seven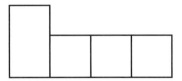

☆ **Challenge**

Draw a Shape Box around each letter:

z e r o   c o u n t   n u m b e r

C Hide and Seek

Name _____

Circle a cookie for each word you spell correctly.

D Other Word Forms

Using the words below, follow instructions given by your teacher.

counted	first	seventh
counting	fourth	sixth
counts	numbers	third
fifth	second	

E Fun Ways to Spell

Initial the box of each activity you finish.

1.

Spell your words with crayons.

3.

Spell your words out loud.

2.

Spell your words with chalk.

4.

Spell your words in damp sand.

Name _____

Use the clues to write the number words in each puzzle.

1. Across

3. Down

1. Down

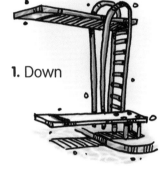

2. Across

3.

3.

2.

4.

2. Down

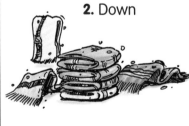

3. Across

4. Across

Word Bank

one	three	five	seven
two	four	six	

G Dictation

Name _____

Listen and write the missing words.

_____ _____ _____ _____

1. _____ _____ _____ _____

_____

_____●

_____ _____ _____ _____

2. _____ _____ _____ _____ ●

_____ _____ _____ _____

3. _____ _____ _____ _____

_____

_____●

H Proofreading

One word in each pair is misspelled.
Fill in the oval by the misspelled word.

1. ○ three
   ○ fuor

4. ○ fiv
   ○ four

☆ ○ numbr
   ○ seven

2. ○ sevin
   ○ two

5. ○ one
   ○ siks

☆ ○ cownt
   ○ first

3. ○ wun
   ○ six

6. ○ thre
   ○ five

☆ ○ have
   ○ zeero

235

I Game

Name _____

Cross out each **a**, **g**, and **p** with a big **X** to find the hidden spelling words. Using one crayon, softly color the boxes you did not mark so you can see your spelling words better.

f	o	u	r	a	a	g	a	a
p	a	g	z	e	r	o	g	g
g	s	e	v	e	n	p	p	p
a	g	a	p	a	g	t	w	o
p	g	c	o	u	n	t	g	p
a	g	g	a	p	p	a	p	g
g	f	i	v	e	g	g	a	a
p	a	a	g	t	h	r	e	e
p	o	n	e	a	g	s	i	x
a	g	n	u	m	b	e	r	a

Remember: Praise God every day for
sending His Son to save you.

J Journaling

Copy and finish one of these sentences:
**It is easy to tell someone about my friend
Jesus when . . .   I talk about Jesus to . . .**

236

A Preview

Write each word as your teacher says it.

Name _____

1. _____

2. _____

3. _____

4. _____

Challenge Words

5. _____

6. _____

7. _____

Scripture

Proverbs 14:14

Write each word in the correct Word Shape Boxes.
Next, in the word Boxes, color the letters that
spell a consonant cluster or digraph in each word.
Circle words that don't contain a cluster or digraph.

Color Words

Lesson 27

1. blue

2. black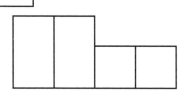

3. brown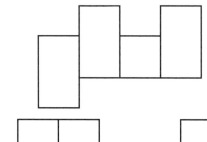

4. green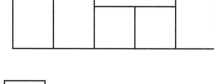

5. yellow

6. white

7. pink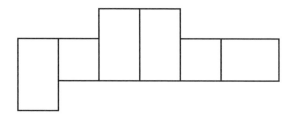

⭐ **Challenge**

Draw a Shape Box around each letter:

o r a n g e   p u r p l e   c o l o r

238

C Hide and Seek

Circle a cookie for each word you spell correctly.

Name _____

D Other Word Forms

Using the words below, follow instructions given by your teacher.

blacker	coloring	pinker
bluest	colors	purples
brownish	greener	whiter
colored	oranges	yellows

E Fun Ways to Spell

Initial the box of each activity you finish.

1.

Spell your words with puzzles.

3.

Spell your words with rhythm instruments.

2.

Spell your words on the clothesline.

4.

Spell your words with shaving cream.

Use the clue to write the color word in each puzzle.

1. A 🐦 is —— —— —— —— ——

2. A | is —— —— —— ——

3. ⚪ are —— —— —— —— ——

4. A 🍌 is —— —— —— —— —— ——

5. A 🌳 is —— —— —— —— ——

6. A 🐤 is —— —— —— —— ——

7. A 🌻 is —— —— —— —— ——

Word Bank

blue	brown	yellow	pink
black	green	white	

Listen and write the missing words.

1. _____ <u>clouds</u> ____ __

_____ ____ ____ <u>sky.</u>

2. ____ <u>sunset</u> ____ ____ .

3. _____ <u>leaves</u> <u>turn</u>

_____ ____ <u>fall.</u>

H Proofreading

One word in each pair is misspelled.
Fill in the oval by the misspelled word.

1. ○ pink
   ○ grene

2. ○ blak
   ○ blue

3. ○ yello
   ○ white

4. ○ brown
   ○ blu

5. ○ penk
   ○ black

6. ○ bronw
   ○ green

☆ ○ colur
   ○ zero

☆ ○ circle
   ○ pirple

☆ ○ aranj
   ○ count

I Game

Daniel had an exciting camping trip with Matthew. Color a campfire next to a tent

each time you or your team spell a word correctly from this week's word list.

Remember: Life is exciting when living for God!

J Journaling

Copy and finish one of these sentences:
Our family went camping and . . .
I've never been camping but . . .

A Preview

Write each word as your teacher says it.

Name _____

1. _____

2. _____

3. _____

4. _____

Challenge Words

5. _____

 _____

6. _____

 _____

7. _____

 _____

Scripture

Proverbs 10:4

B Word Shapes

Write each word in the correct Word Shape Boxes.

1. little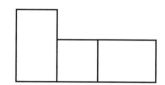

2. tall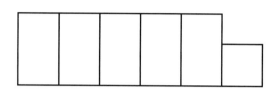

3. short

4. long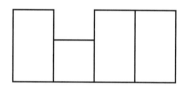

5. few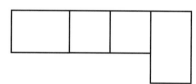

6. many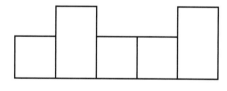

7. more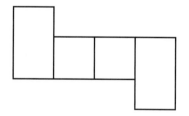

 Challenge

Draw a Shape Box around each letter:

t h i n   t h i c k   d i g i t

C Hide and Seek

Name _____

Circle a cookie for each word you spell correctly.

D Other Word Forms

Using the words below, follow instructions given by your teacher.

digits	littlest	shorter	thicker
fewer	longer	shortest	thickest
fewest	longest	taller	thinner
littler	most	tallest	thinnest

E Fun Ways to Spell

Initial the box of each activity you finish.

1.

Spell your words with crayons.

3.

Spell your words out of the letter box.

2.

Spell your words with an eraser.

4.

Spell your words with finger paint.

F **Word Find**

Find and circle
the words.

Name _____

Size and Quantity Words

Lesson
28

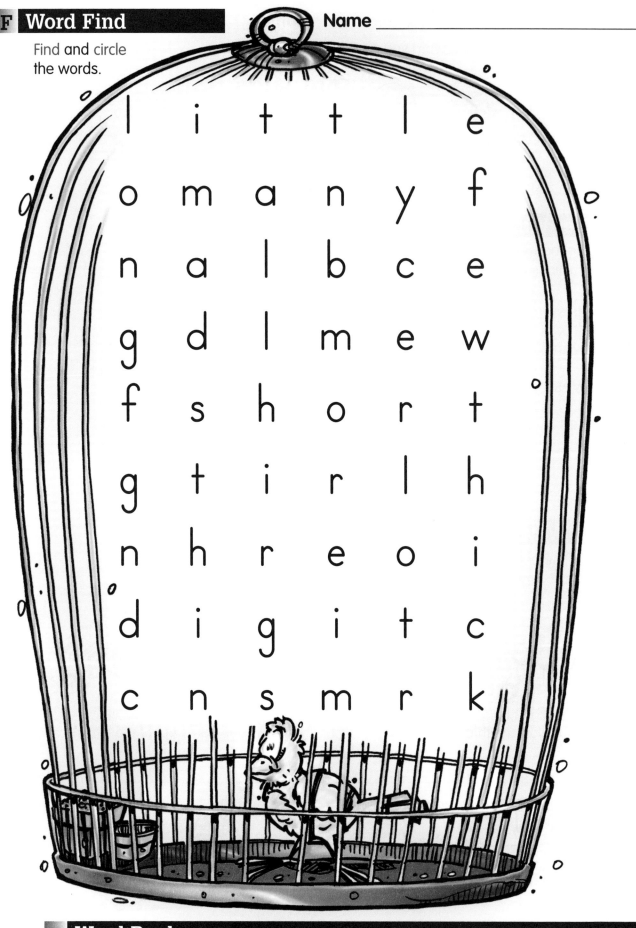

l i t t l e

o m a n y f

n a l b c e

g d l m e w

f s h o r t

g t i r l h

n h r e o i

d i g i t c

c n s m r k

Word Bank

| little | short | few | more | ☆ thick |
| tall | long | many | ☆ thin | ☆ digit |

G Dictation

Name _____

Listen and write the missing words.

1. A _____ ant came,
   _____ _____ _____
   _____ _____ _____•

2. _____ _____ a _____ _____•

3. _____ _____ legs _____
   _____ _____
   _____ _____•

H Proofreading

One word in each pair is misspelled.
Fill in the oval by the misspelled word.

1. ○ tall
   ○ shurt

2. ○ liddl
   ○ long

3. ○ more
   ○ miny

4. ○ fue
   ○ short

5. ○ little
   ○ tol

6. ○ many
   ○ mor

☆ ○ dijit
   ○ orange

☆ ○ color
   ○ thik

☆ ○ none
   ○ htin

I Game

Place a game piece over each word your teacher says and spells. When you get five game pieces in a row, raise your hand and say, "Spelling is fun!"

tooth	tall	first	books	thin
circle	more	purple	enjoy	long
above	thick	**FREE** orange		many
soon	few	have	zero	digit
Lord	little	none	hasn't	short

little	digit	long	many	tall
zero	orange	more	count	books
thick	have	**FREE**	none	first
have	circle	short	green	thin
above	soon	few	six	two

Remember: God blesses hard work.

J Journaling

Choose a job that helps at home.
Write a note telling what you plan to do.
Copy your note to give to mom or dad.

A Test-Words

Write each word as your teacher says it.

1. _____

2. _____

3. _____

4. _____

5. _____

6. _____

☆ Test-Challenge Words

Write each challenge word
as your teacher says it.

Scripture

Psalm 98:6

B **Game**

In the story from lesson 29, as Tommy watched the ants make their way across the backyard, he understood what his dad had meant. He could make a joyful symphony to the Lord no matter how small his part in the school program. Circle one ant for each review word you or your team spell correctly.

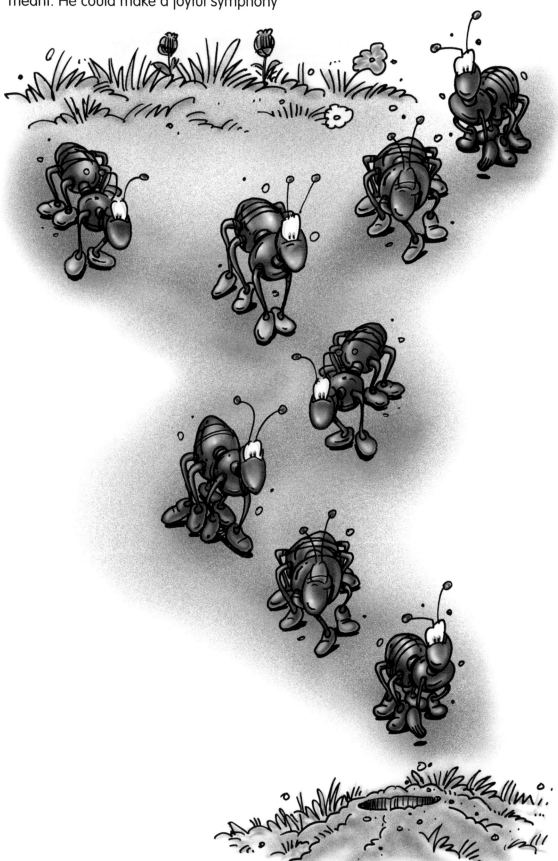

Name _____

The underlined word in each sentence is misspelled. Write the sentences on the lines below, spelling each underlined word correctly.

I like the <u>wite</u> kitten.

1. _____

Tommy was <u>siks</u> years old.

2. _____

D **Test-Proofreading**

One word in each pair is misspelled.
Fill in the oval by the misspelled word.

1. ⬭ hsort   **4.** ⬭ bron
⬭ three   ⬭ short

2. ⬭ mor   **5.** ⬭ pinc
⬭ seven   ⬭ long

3. ⬭ brown   **6.** ⬭ more
⬭ thre   ⬭ sevn

⭐ **Test-Challenge Words**

Write each challenge word
as your teacher says it.

Christopher, Kristin, and Cathy need to earn money to buy their mom a canary for her birthday. Help them with their work by moving one space each time you or your team spell a review word correctly.

F Test-Sentence

The underlined word in this sentence is misspelled. Write the sentence on the lines below, spelling the underlined word correctly.

The ants crawled in a <u>lawng</u> line.

_____

_____

_____

_____

G Test-Words

Write each word as your teacher says it.

1. _____

2. _____

3. _____

4. _____

5. _____

6. _____

☆ Test-Challenge Words

Write each challenge word as your teacher says it.

Write about how you worked with a group to do something important.

Remember: Even little things, done well,
can bring great results.

Spelling Is Fun!

This certificate is awarded to:

_____

_____

for practicing these Spelling words, completing
fun activities, and playing great learning games!

_____

Date: _____

one	blue	little
two	black	tall
three	brown	short
four	green	long
five	yellow	few
six	white	many
seven	pink	more
☆ zero	☆ orange	☆ thin
☆ count	☆ purple	☆ thick
☆ number	☆ color	☆ digit